UNDERWATER
NATURALIST
MANUAL

PADI®
padi.com

Acknowledgments

Editor in Chief
Drew Richardson, Ed.D.

Instructional Design, Development, Consultation and Review
Lesley Alexander, Ph.D.; Mark Caney; Pascal Dietrich; Mike Holme; Yasushi Inoue; Brigit Jaeger; John Kinsella; Jenny Miller Garmendia; Steve Mortell; Suzanne Pleydell; Julie Taylor Sanders; Karl Shreeves, M.A.; Trond Skaare; Linda Van Velsan

Graphic Design and Production
Kimberly Sickel

Photography
Jurg Beeli, Budd Riker, Karl Shreeves, Bob Wohlers

Production and Coordination
Lori Bachelor-Smith; Heather Goodwin-Robinson, Ted Moreta; Joshua Stewart

Underwater Naturalist *Manual*

© PADI 2008

Published by PADI
30151 Tomas
Rancho Santa Margarita, CA 92688-2125

Produced by Diving Science & Technology for PADI.

ISBN 978-1-878663-83-2

Printed in the United States of America

Product No. 79186 (6/08) Version 1.0

Table of Contents

Introduction

Ask divers why they dive and "to see aquatic life" or "to enjoy nature's underwater beauty" is virtually always one of the main reasons. For many divers (especially nature photographers), this is *the* reason to dive, and even the most ardent, hardcore tekkie "I'm-in-it-for-the-adventure" divers rank observing nature underwater as a primary reason they dive. Clearly, an appreciation for nature and diving go together.

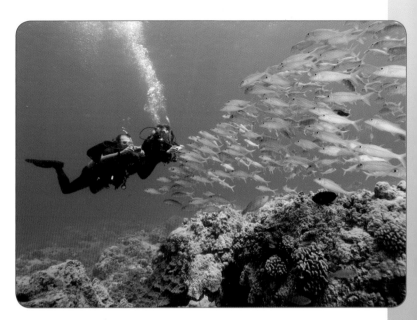

On the other hand, nature's most wondrous intricacy can unfold before most divers' eyes, and they will totally miss it. Novices quickly pick up the names for the most common and prettiest sea creatures, but it takes a more informed diver to recognize the interrelationships between organisms or understand why seemingly harmless interactions, like feeding or petting fish, can hurt organisms or the environment.

The goal of the PADI Underwater Naturalist course is to help you progress from someone who enjoys nature to someone who sees not only organisms, but their roles, relationships and place in the ecosystem. As a PADI Underwater Naturalist, you'll better recognize how your presence affects the aquatic world, and steps you can take to minimize negative effects. You'll also develop a background in several ways science organizes and classifies living things, each to provide a different basis for understanding them.

Course Overview

As with most PADI Specialty Diver courses, the PADI Underwater Naturalist course emphasizes diving, and you will make at least two underwater naturalist dives in open water with your PADI Instructor. You'll establish your background in underwater natural history and key science concepts with this manual.

You'll have fun on these dives while developing your underwater naturalist skills based on knowledge development you'll cover by reading this manual and by discussing the material with your instructor prior to your dives. Your instructor may decide to have more formal class meetings or practice sessions. The recommended sequence is to begin by skimming through this manual, noting the headings, topics and pictures. This speeds learning by giving you an idea of where you're headed. Then, as you read, highlight or underline the answers to the study objectives. **It's important to actually do this** - not simply note them - because the physical act of writing/highlighting enhances transferring the knowledge to long-term memory. Answer the exercises, reviewing anything you don't understand. Then, fill out the Knowledge Reviews to turn in to your instructor.

Although not required, your instructor may have you initially practice some skills in a pool or confined water,

PADI Underwater Naturalist Course Prerequisites

To take the PADI Underwater Naturalist course, you must be certified as a PADI (Junior) Open Water Diver or have a qualifying certification from another training organization similar to that of a PADI Open Water Diver.

If you'll be diving deeper than 18 metres/60 feet, it's recommended that you successfully complete the PADI Deep Diver course. This course develops your knowledge and skills appropriate for diving to an absolute maximum depth of 40 metres/130 feet.

such as environmentally friendly diving techniques. Your instructor may also assign some fun projects related to studying underwater nature, and will review what you've been studying as part of your predive briefings. Because different environments have different organisms, your instructor will brief you on specifics about the aquatic animals and environment you'll be observing and interacting with.

When you've completed the course, you'll have earned the PADI Underwater Naturalist certification. With your PADI Underwater Naturalist certification, you can apply for the Master Scuba Diver rating if you also have a PADI Advanced Open Water Diver and a PADI Rescue Diver (or qualifying certification from another training organization); with certification in four other PADI specialty certifications, and you have 50-logged dives.

The PADI Underwater Naturalist certification credits toward the PADI Master Scuba Diver rating - recreational diving's highest nonprofessional level.

Other Skills You'll Want as a PADI Underwater Naturalist

You'll apply your skills and knowledge as a PADI Underwater Naturalist on almost every dive because even the seemingly "barren" underwater environments are complex ecosystems worth observing. However, you'll find being an Underwater Naturalist goes especially well with the skills you develop in the following PADI Specialty Diver courses:

- **AWARE-Fish Identification** - This course overlaps with and extends what you learn in the PADI Underwater Naturalist course. Besides broadening your familiarity with Project AWARE (Aquatic World Awareness, Responsibility and Education), you learn more about

fish species and how you can help scientists monitor the oceans' health by participating in underwater fish surveys.

- **Project AWARE** – Familiarize yourself with the role Project AWARE plays in protecting worldwide aquatic ecosystems. Learn about the potential issues concerning the environmental status of worldwide aquatic ecosystems such as fisheries concerns, coastal management, and marine pollution. This course highlights initiatives that you can participate in to protect the aquatic environment.

- **PADI Night Diver** – After sunset, the undersea "night shift" comes out, and that means different organisms, different behaviors and different interactions. The PADI Night Diver course introduces you to diving after dark, opening the door to exploring the nocturnal side of nature.

- **PADI Deep Diver** – Because there's less light, less wave motion and typically cooler temperatures, below 18 metres/60 feet you'll often find different organisms and natural characteristics than you do in the shallows. The best way to learn about the considerations and procedures for deep recreational diving is to complete the PADI Deep Diver course. The PADI Deep Diver training prepares you to enjoy discovering nature's secrets below 18 metres/60 feet.

- **PADI Digital Underwater Photographer or Videographer** – Shooting pictures or video of underwater wildlife are a natural extension of being a PADI Underwater Naturalist. It's a great way to document your observations for further study later. Artistically speaking, divers and nondivers alike find photos or videos more interesting when you tell them what they're looking at and why it's significant. Either way, underwater imaging and naturalism make a great skill set.

- **PADI Peak Performance Buoyancy Diver** - It's useful to fine-tune your buoyancy skills for all diving, but philosophically, it's almost expected that PADI Underwater Naturalists control their buoyancy with the utmost precision. That's because the better you control your buoyancy, the more you minimize incidental contact with your surroundings, which is the best way to avoid harming sensitive marine organisms or damaging fragile parts of shipwrecks.

- **PADI Dry Suit Diver** - Many cooler water environments support prolific underwater communities. Dry suits give you access to some of these for longer dives than you can make in a wet suit. In the cases of the

Watch for These Symbols

 Alerts you to important safety information. Pay close attention when you see this symbol and consult your instructor if you do not understand the material.

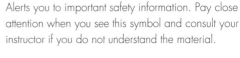 Reminds you to interact harmoniously with the aquatic environment while highlighting relevant information or a specific diving technique.

 Alerts you to additional/related information on PADI videos, books, CD-ROM and other media. This material is for your interest and further learning. The information required for this course is in this manual.

coldest climates, *only* a dry suit allows you to dive, yet some of these environments have abundant and interesting organisms found nowhere else.

The first dive of most PADI specialties* corresponds to the same dive in the PADI Adventures in Diving program. Therefore, if you're a PADI Advanced Open Water Diver or Adventure Diver, you may have already made the first dive to these specialty courses. Similarly, the first dive of the specialties credits toward the Advanced Open Water Diver or Adventure Diver certification.

Successfully completing five PADI Specialties, a PADI Advanced Open Water Diver and a PADI Rescue Diver (or qualifying certification from another training organization) and 50-logged dives qualifies you for the PADI Master Scuba Diver rating - the highest nonprofessional rating in the sport.

For more information about PADI courses, including specialties, the Adventures in Diving program and PADI Master Scuba Diver, visit padi.com.

*PADI Ice Diver, Cavern Diver, Semiclosed Rebreather courses and TecRec courses do not have corresponding dives in the Adventures in Diving program.

Introduction to the
Aquatic Realm

It may seem odd to have an "introduction" to the aquatic realm when, as a certified diver, you've obviously been introduced to it already. While you may have hundreds of dives logged and recognize dozens of different aquatic animals, it may be that you've never looked at the underwater realm from an objective, science-based naturalist's perspective. Taking that point of view requires understanding the concepts of ecosystems, and recognizing how the differing characteristics you find underwater versus on land shape the nature of their respective ecosystems.

Ecology and Ecosystems

Since the late 1960s and the rise of environmental awareness, *ecology* has gone from a term used by a few scientists to a media buzzword that you hear in casual conversations. Yet despite its transition into common usage, many people don't understand what ecology means, or what an *ecosystem* is, beyond recognizing that they're important and are related to health of our planet.

Ecology is the study of living things and their interrelations with each other and with their environment.

When we study ecology, we're concerned with the *abiotic* components (physical characteristics) such as non-living chemicals, temperature, gases, light and the *biotic* components (organic characteristics) such as other organisms and organically produced chemicals.

An *ecosystem* (also call a *biome*) is a natural system that functions as a unit and consists of all the living organisms in a defined area interacting with each other and non-living physical factors.

How you define an ecosystem can be broad or specific, with larger ecosystems consisting of many smaller ecosystems. It depends upon what you're studying. A puddle of rainwater can be considered an ecosystem, so can an entire coastline. Ultimately, millions and millions of ecosystems exist within the earth's single ecosystem. This overlap shows us that while ecosystems function as individual systems, they also interact with each other as part of larger systems, and that no ecosystem is entirely independent. You could compare this with an automobile, which operates as a single unit, yet accomplishes its different functions through many interdependent but distinct subsystems.

The two broadest ecosystems are terrestrial (land) and aquatic (water), each with their own sub ecosystems.

Major terrestrial ecosystems include tundra, taiga, grassland, temperate forest, desert, tropical rain forest and chaparral. The major aquatic ecosystems are fresh water and marine (ocean). The ocean is an ecosystem, with its many smaller ecosystems, and is the largest biome.

Community and Habitats

A *community* is a collection of different organisms living and interacting in an ecosystem. This includes all species and types of organisms. A *population* is a group of the same species living and interacting within a community. This interaction is part of the definition because sometimes two populations of the same species live in a single community. An example of this exists off Vancouver Island, Canada. In these waters, orca pods live relatively closely together, yet maintain separate populations that rarely interact. These pods don't even interbreed as far as scientists can tell. Therefore, separate pods would be considered separate populations within a community.

A *habitat* includes the area and conditions in which you find an organism. Some species are adapted to or occur in very specific habitats, whereas others range over a variety of habitats. Chitons, for example, live in the rocky intertidal zone, whereas octopuses live in a wide depth range and in many different parts of the reef. The chiton has a narrowly defined habitat compared to the octopus. A *microhabitat* exists on a very small scale. For example, tiny crustaceans and worms live in the spaces between sand grains on the sea floor.

An organism's role in its habitat is called its *niche*. Very different species can occupy the same niche. On coral reefs, for example, cleaner-shrimp and cleaner-fish both survive by feeding on parasites and dead or injured skin of reef fish. To avoid confusing habitat and niche, think of the habitat as an organism's address, and the niche as it's job.

Terrestrial and Aquatic Ecosystems

It's obvious that there are many aquatic organisms that differ significantly from terrestrial organisms, and vice versa. This is often because the physical and structural differences between terrestrial and aquatic ecosystems impose differing demands and therefore adaptations.

Terrestrial Physical Characteristics. Terrestrial ecosystems exist in air, which is the primary difference from water that results in many of the other physical differences. Air is not very dense (about 800 times less dense than water), and dealing with air resistance isn't an issue for many organisms. Air movement has some effects, but relatively few organisms distribute spores/seed via the wind. Few organisms travel long distance by wind, which encourages relatively isolated, distinct species populations. Excepting birds, even the fastest terrestrial animals have less streamlining compared to aquatic animals.

Light penetrates air well, and excepting caves, similar levels of light reaches all terrestrial ecosystems. While shading is a factor, other than absorbing ultraviolet light (which is very important), air doesn't alter the spectral qualities of light significantly. The vast majority of terrestrial organisms adapted to darkness are nocturnal rather than organisms that live in a perpetually dark environment.

All terrestrial organisms deal with the effects of gravity. Terrestrial organisms require support structures that are made out of fiber, wood, bone, cartilage etc.; the larger the organism, the more support structure it needs. An elephant with its massive bones to carry its size is an example, and even a tiny insect has a rigid exoskeleton.

Terrestrial organisms must deal with the downward pull of gravity when they move, by friction (crawling like a snake), expending energy directly against it (climbing/flying) or by shifting and pivoting weight from one limb to another (walking). The larger the organism, the more energy this requires. Because of the high-energy demands of terrestrial existence, biochemically, terrestrial organisms tend to be higher in fat and carbohydrates (primary energy sources) than aquatic organisms.

Oxygen exists with relatively even distribution in the atmosphere (about 21 percent), making terrestrial environments with less than this very rare (a few caves, for example). The vast majority of organisms adapted to low oxygen conditions live at high altitudes.

 See Dalton's Law in the Chemistry and Physics of Diving section of *The Encyclopedia of Recreational Diving*.

Learn more...

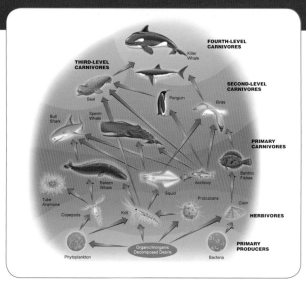

Food chains interconnect as food webs, which show feeding relationships within an ecosystem. Food chains/webs always begin with a primary producer and end with an animal.

Terrestrial Structural Characteristics. Plants dominate most terrestrial ecosystems and we think of those ecosystems in plant terms: redwood forests, grass prairies, oak woodlands, etc. This is because dominating plants are large, long-lived flowering plants that need massive structures to stand erect against gravity. Such plants are not easy to remove from the environment, so relatively stable, long-lived plant communities control relatively short-lived animal communities.

Food chains, food webs and *food networks* are ways of describing the feeding relationships between species in an ecosystem. In other words, they're a map of what eats what. In a basic food chain, each link (organism) is a source of energy and material (food) for the next link. Until you begin looking at very specialized ecosystems, food chains begin with a *primary producer* (plant or other photosynthesizing organism) that harnesses energy from the sun, and end with an animal. Since most organisms are part of more than one food chain because they eat more than one kind of food, interconnected food chains form a food web or network.

Food chains or webs are grouped into *trophic* (nourishment) levels that are based on how far removed organisms at a particular level are from the primary producers. The more levels an ecosystem has in its food web, the more energy and material must pass from one level to the next.

Terrestrial food chains tend to be short because it takes large animals to eat large plants, and because each trophic level uses more energy to meet the demands of terrestrial existence. An example of a terrestrial food chain might be grass eaten by an antelope, which in turn is eaten by a lion. This is a food chain with three links.

Aquatic Physical Characteristics. Compared to air, water is a high density medium (about 800 times denser), which produces profound differences compared to terrestrial ecosystems. The first of these is that it allows many organisms of all sizes – microscopic to many times larger than a human – to live suspended for extended periods. Some species live their entire lives in the water column. This is particularly true of the *plankton* (from the Greek word meaning *wanderers*) community. There is no terrestrial equivalent to plankton. On the other hand, water resistance restricts movement. Excepting sedentary organisms and those that move very slowly or crawl on the bottom, the vast majority of aquatic organisms are streamlined. Even relatively slow animals like manatees have a streamlined shape.

Water movement plays a significant role in both feeding and reproduction. The flow of water redistributes nutrients and organisms, so that in the oceans, some food webs rely on energy carried to organisms that consume primary producers elsewhere. Plankton is a major food source; the largest animals on earth, the baleen whales, feed on plankton.

Currents distribute larvae (young) over a wide area, making species distribution relatively wide. Many organisms distribute sperm, spores or eggs through water movement. This is true even in relatively isolated aquatic ecosystems such as inland lakes.

Water absorbs light, so that sunlight only penetrates to a maximum depth of about 180 metres/600 feet, and that only in the clearest water. Furthermore, water absorbs light asymmetrically, taking up red first, then orange, yellow, green and finally blue. This restricts plants and other photosynthetic organisms to the upper, lit areas of the water column. Where the water is consistently turbid, photosynthesizers may be limited to the first metre/three feet or less. Even in clear water, absorption by color affects the vertical distribution of plants because different species use different parts of the spectrum for photosynthesis.

Many aquatic communities (fresh and salt water) are perpetually dark and are home to organisms adapted to life there. Most of these thrive based on nutrients that sink from shallower water, though some deep-water communities, such as those by hydrothermal vents, depend on chemical energy sources for energy. In these

See Water and Light in the Chemistry and Physics of Diving section of *The Encyclopedia of Recreational Diving.*

Learn more...

ecosystems, chemosynthesizers – bacteria harnessing energy from chemicals – take on the role that plants and other photosynthesizers play by harnessing from light.

In water, buoyancy substantially offsets gravity, and vertical motion is relatively easy. This allows organisms to grow very large without rigid structures for support. Those organisms with structures such as fish and marine mammals use the structures to allow them to move quickly. Even animals with rigid structures become larger in the aquatic environment. Whales are the largest animals known to have lived, out sizing even the largest dinosaurs by many times. Gravity isn't gone due to buoyancy – most organisms still orient up and down based on it – but buoyancy saves tremendous energy because organisms don't have to fight gravity to move.

Compared to terrestrial organisms, aquatic organisms are high in protein and low in fat and carbohydrates (there are exceptions, including marine mammals and cold-water fish like salmon). This reflects a low energy existence.

Oxygen distribution in water is typically uneven, and varies with depth and conditions. Water that's agitated such as surf may be high in oxygen, whereas stagnant, deep water may be much lower in oxygen. Different species may have differing gill adaptations for these conditions.

Aquatic Structural Characteristics. Most aquatic ecosystems are dominated by animals, and we tend to think of them in animal terms, such as coral reefs, oyster banks, clam beds, mussel beds and so on. This is because aquatic plants and other photosynthesizers (primary producers) are small and exist in huge numbers. Their population tends to vary seasonally as the amount of sunlight varies.

Because they're small, aquatic primary producers are food for very small animals, particularly *copepods* in the marine environment. Copepods are tiny shrimp-like animals that larger organisms like fish feed upon. As *primary consumers,* copepods are crucial to the ecosystem because they pass the energy harnessed by the primary producers into the food web.

In the aquatic world, long-lived animal populations control short-lived plant/photosynthetic organisms that get eaten rapidly. One notable exception to this is the kelp forest, which is a large algae dominated ecosystem.

Food chains tend to be longer in aquatic ecosystems, and food webs are more complex. An example aquatic food chain might be: phytoplankton (photosynthetic plankton) eaten by a copepod, which is then eaten by herring, then the herring is eaten by a squid, and finally the squid is eaten by a shark. This is a five-link food chain. The long chains demonstrate that each trophic level tends to use less energy than each level in a typical terrestrial food web. However, it's worth noting that many of the largest aquatic animals – whales and whale sharks – feed on plankton in which primary producers and primary consumers predominate. This eliminates many of the intermediate trophic layers.

Relationships among Aquatic Animals

Now let's look at the relationships that you find between aquatic animals as they interact in a particular ecosystem. During your PADI Underwater Naturalist dives, you'll be looking for examples of these relationships as well as identifying taxa for organisms you observe.

Predator/prey relationships. The most common interrelationship between aquatic animals is predator and prey. This is simply the process of one animal eating another, and provides the primary way that energy moves up through aquatic food webs. Recall that in terrestrial food webs, it's common for large animals to eat photosynthesizers, greatly shortening food chains.

Some examples of predator/prey are very obvious to even novice divers and those inexperienced with underwater naturalism: grouper eats snapper, largemouth bass eats minnow, orca eats seal, octopus eats lobster and so on. Other forms of predation aren't as obvious. A sea star eating a clam is a long, slow event by human standards. You can see damselfish feeding on plankton, but their prey is so small that to the uninitiated, it just looks like they're flapping their lips.

Most aquatic ecosystems are dominated by animals. We tend to think of them in animal terms, such as this coral reef.

Because energy moves through food webs through predation, a skillful diver can observe a species in its role as both predator and prey. An example may be a small freshwater bluegill (sunfish) eats a tadpole, then a largemouth bass eats the bluegill.

Symbiosis. *Symbiosis* is the relationship of animals of different species living together in close association. There are different forms of symbiosis depending upon how the association benefits, fails to benefit, or harms the organisms in the association.

Mutualism is a symbiosis in which both species benefit from the association. A common example of mutualism is the *Ocellaris* clownfish living in the tentacles of the *Ritteri* sea anemone. The clownfish protects the anemone from predators that eat anemones, and the anemone's stinging tentacles protect the clownfish from predators that eat clownfish. A special mucus coating protects the clownfish from the anemone's sting.

The sea anemone-clownfish relationship is an example of mutualism, *which is symbiosis in which both organisms benefit from the relationship. In this example, the anemone and the clownfish protect each other from predation.*

Commensalism is symbiosis in which one species clearly benefits, but the other species doesn't benefit, but it's not harmed. One example of this is the remora that attach to large shark species. The remora benefits by getting a free ride and sometimes by getting food scraps as the

Photograph © Jurg Beeli

The remora-shark relationship is an example of commensalism. The remora benefits with neither harm nor benefit to the shark.

shark feeds. The host doesn't benefit, but the remora doesn't harm it either.

Some indirect dependencies can be confused with commensalism, though they're not actually because the organisms don't live in association. Hermit crabs, for example, depend upon the shells of gastropods to protect themselves. Although only one species benefits and the other isn't harmed directly, this isn't commensalism because the species don't live in association with each other.

Parasitism is symbiosis in which the parasite (one species) benefits at the expense (harm) of the host (the other species). In most instances, the parasite obtains food, while the host suffers from reduced food intake, lowered resistance to disease, injury or a general loss of vigor. The host may die due to being weakened by the parasite, making it more vulnerable to predation or disease, but not directly due to the parasite. One example is parasitic copepods that live on the skin of fish. They feed on the fish's tissue, which creates irritation and opens their flesh to infection. Other common aquatic parasites are worms that live inside sea animals' digestive systems, taking food and weakening the host.

9

Exercise 1 – Introduction to the Aquatic Realm

1. Ecology is
   - ☐ a. the political effort to save the environment.
   - ☐ b. the study of living things and their interrelations with each other and with their environment.
   - ☐ c. Both a and b.
   - ☐ d. None of the above.

2. Physical and structural characteristics of aquatic ecosystems include (check all that apply):
   - ☐ a. low density medium.
   - ☐ b. high density medium.
   - ☐ c. unevenly dispersed oxygen.
   - ☐ d. evenly dispersed oxygen.
   - ☐ e. light reaches virtually all ecosystems.
   - ☐ f. light does not reach many ecosystems.
   - ☐ g. effects of gravity reduced.
   - ☐ h. organisms require rigid structure and expend more energy.
   - ☐ i. ecosystems tend to be animal dominated.

3. Symbiosis is defined as
   - ☐ a. a relationship in which two animals of different species live in close association.
   - ☐ b. a relationship in which two animals of different species benefit from close association.
   - ☐ c. a relationship in which one animal benefits and another animal neither benefits nor is harmed from close association.
   - ☐ d. a relationship in which one animal benefits at the expense of another animal in a close association.

4. A cleaner shrimp removes parasitic organisms and dead tissue from the skin and scales of fish. The shrimp benefits by obtaining food, and the fish benefits by having the parasites removed. This is an example of
   - ☐ a. mutualism.
   - ☐ b. commensalism.
   - ☐ c. parasitism.
   - ☐ d. None of the above.

How'd you do?
1. b. *2.* b, c, f, g, i. *3.* a. *4.* a.

The Linnaeus *Classification System*

"What's in a name? That which we call a rose by any other name would smell as sweet," says Shakespeare's Juliet in his famous play, *Romeo and Juliet*. And, while no poet then or now would argue with the master playwright's semantics, modern naturalists and biologists would argue that using multiple names for a single species stinks because it causes a lot of confusion!

As a PADI Underwater Naturalist, you need a basic understanding of the Linnaeus classification system because it is the basis for the unique scientific name every distinct species has. While you'll still use common names, even when talking with scientists and fellow naturalists, when it comes to documentation and research you'll need to use an organism's scientific name.

The Need for Classification

There are at least three reasons why science classifies organisms and assigns scientific names according to the classifications. The first reason is that classification helps identify a particular organism's relationships with other organisms. Classification makes it easier to determine how organisms are similar and different, which

Study Objectives

Underline/highlight the answers to these questions as you read:

1. What are three reasons scientists have for classifying organisms?

2. What are the seven main taxa into which scientists classify organisms?

3. What two taxa does an organism's scientific name represent?

4. How do taxonomists determine into which taxon to classify an organism?

5. What common problem do taxonomists have in classifying organisms and how do they solve it?

6. What are the six-kingdom and three-domain systems of classification?

becomes the basis for giving order to the millions of life forms known to exist.

A second reason for classification is that it requires scientists to identify the key characteristics of each organism clearly. This close examination avoids (or at least greatly reduces the probability) that two variations of the same organism will be mistaken for two different organisms. It also helps scientists recognize organisms that are very similar and related, and others that are very similar but not closely related.

Third, classification helps avoid confusion. Common names for organisms differ with culture, language and location, so two different organisms may have the same common name. One example in English is the name "dolphin," which may mean a marine mammal or the food fish also known as "mahi-mahi" or "el dorado."

The common name "dolphin," which may mean a marine mammal or a food fish also known as "mahi-mahi" or "el dorado." Scientists, however, call these two species Tursiops truncatus *and* Coryphaena hippurus, *respectively, and there is no confusion.*

Regardless of nationality, scientists call these two species *Tursiops truncatus* and *Coryphaena hippurus*, respectively, and there is no confusion. When a scientist hears, reads or writes the species' scientific name, there is no question about the exact species in question.

Classification Taxa

Science divides all organisms into divisions and subdivisions using the Linnaeus classification system, named after the Swedish botanist Carolus Linnaeus who introduced it in 1758. The divisions are call *taxa* (singular *taxon*), with taxa within taxa. Each taxon has a unique Latin name that identifies it. Scientists who assign organisms to the respective divisions are called taxonomists.

The most specific taxon is species, which is unique to an individual type of organism. The most general taxon is kingdom, which are large groups of different organisms that share very broad characteristics. There are seven main taxa into which scientists classify organisms. Ranging from the most specific to the most general, these are:

Species – This is the most specific taxa and identifies an individual type of organism. A species is considered to be a group of organisms that can reproduce together to produce fertile offspring. When referring to a particular organism, the convention is to use both the genus (next

Does it Have to be Latin?

Newcomers to science sometimes wonder why scientific names are all from Latin. How did it start? Is it important?

Scientific names were originally Latin because in Linnaeus' time, scholars used Latin. It was the common language used by all scientists, much as English is today.

Latin has stayed on as the basis for scientific names for at least two apparent reasons. The first is tradition. The world has grown accustomed to it, so that when scientists see a binomial (two part) Latin name, they recognize it as the scientific name. A second reason is that since all organisms have only one scientific name, Latin provides a neutral language. No one from any culture need feel slighted because scientific names are in another

scientist's native language. Today, Latin is no one's native language.

It's worth noting that while scientific names are in Latin form, not all scientific names originate from the Latin language. Sometimes a species takes the name of the discoverer of that species or in honor of someone. For instance, a new species of penguin discovered by Dr. Smith might be called *Spheniscus smithus*. It's also common for the name of a classification to borrow from Greek. For example, the phylum Arthropoda (includes crustaceans and insects) gets its name from the Greek *arthro* meaning *jointed* and *podos* meaning *foot*.

taxon level) and species, such as *Homo sapiens,* the Latin name for human. It's also customary to italicize genus and species, but not any other level's scientific name.

Genus (plural genera) – This is the taxon above species. Species within a genus are considered to be closely related. For example, there are 34 species of reef shark that all belong to the genus *Carcharhinus.* When referring to all the species in a specific genus, it is common to use the form Genus sp.; the 34 reef sharks may be referred to as *Carcharhinus sp.* (sp. for species).

Family – Genera that share characteristics are grouped into a family. As an example, *Carcharhinus* and several other shark genera make up the shark family Carcharhinidae, which consists of 51 species.

Order – Related families are grouped into orders. Continuing the example, family Carcharhinidae is in order Carcharhiniformes along with the Sphynidae (hammerhead), Scyliorhinidae (catsharks) and other families. About 260 species make up this order.

Class – Classes group related orders together. Class Chondrichthyes includes the order Carcharhiniformes and several other orders of sharks, rays and their close relatives, accounting for more than 1000 species.

Phylum/Division – Classes are grouped together by phylum or division (botanists usually use divisions to classify plants). Phyla (plural of phylum) are groupings of animals based on general body plans, so they may look quite different externally while sharing an internal organization. For example, Chondrichthyes along with the classes for mammals, birds, reptiles, amphibians and bony fish belong to phylum Chordata, which groups together all animals that have a notochord and a dorsal nerve cord during either development or their entire lives. Most species are vertebrates, meaning these take the form of a spinal cord and backbone, but there are some species that have a different type of notochord and dorsal nerve cord.

Kingdom – Phyla group together into kingdoms. For example, Phylum Chordata and 32 other phyla make up kingdom Animalia – the animal kingdom. Although there are approximately 33 phyla, during the PADI Underwater Naturalist course you'll focus primarily on seven that account for the majority of underwater species you'll encounter: Porifera, Cnidaria, Annelida, Mollusca, Arthropoda, Echinodermata and Chordata.

Phylum	Meaning	Group	Distinguishing Characteristics	Species Identified
Porifera	Pore bearer	Sponges	Perforated interior wall	about 5000
Cnidaria	Stinging nettle	Coelenterates	Nematocysts (stinging cells)	about 11,000
Annelida	Little ring	Segmented worms	Multiple circular segments	about 15,000
Mollusca	Thin shell	Mollusks/Molluscs	Muscular foot and mantle round shell	about 112,000
Arthropoda	Jointed foot	Arthropods	Chitin exoskeleton	Over 1,000,000,134,000+
Echinodermata	Spiny skin	Echinoderms	Five-fold radial symmetry, mesodermal calcified spines	about 7000 living species and 13,000 extinct ones
Chordata	Cord	Chordates	Hollow dorsal nervous chord	about 100,000+

Science divides all organisms into divisions and subdivisions using the Linnaeus classification system, which has divisions called taxa *(singular* taxon*).*

Determining Taxa

In creating taxa, taxonomists use two primary methods. When classifying multicellular, complex organisms, most taxonomists do so based on anatomical features. This usually works well and shows possible relationships between organisms. Until relatively recently, anatomical features were the only basis available for classifying organisms, but the study of genetics has changed this. Taxonomists may therefore also compare the DNA of different species to determine taxa. This is particularly useful for classifying single-celled organisms that differ very little anatomically.

On paper, the Linnaeus classification system ought to work very well with everything fitting neatly into kingdoms, phyla, classes, orders and so on, but a common problem taxonomists have is that some organisms or groups of organisms don't fit cleanly into defined taxa. Sometimes organisms have characteristics that put it into a specific taxon, yet other characteristics that separate them from it. Yet, these organisms don't really fit into a taxon above or below either.

Taxonomists solve this problem by creating intermediate super (above) or sub (below) categories between the normal levels. For example, consider sharks and rays. Both belong to the class Chondrichthyes, which includes all fish with a cartilage skeleton. The next level below (order) would divide all sharks and rays, but it creates a difficulty: clearly sharks and rays make up two clear groups, but you would end up with several orders of sharks and several orders of rays. Taxonomists solved this by creating super order Selachimorpha, which encompasses the shark orders, and super order Batoidea, which encompasses the ray orders. Taxonomists add these levels as necessary so that taxa group and divide organisms according to their shared similarities and differences.

Comparison of Super- and Sublevels of Classification

	California Horn Shark	Spotted Eagle Ray
Kingdom	Animalia	Animalia
Phylum	Chordata	Chordata
Subphylum	Vertebrata	Vertebrata
Superclass	Gnathostomata (jawed vertebrates)	Gnathostomata (jawed vertebrates)
Class	Chondrichthyes (rays, sharks, and relatives)	Chondrichthyes (rays, sharks, and relatives)
Subclass	Elasmobranchii (sharks)	Elasmobranchii (sharks)
Superorder	Selachimorpha	Batidoidimorpha
Order	Heterodontiformes	Rajiformes (rays, sawfishes, and skates)
Family	Heterodontidae	Myliobatoidea
Subfamily		Myliobatinae
Genus	Heterodontus	Aetobatus
Species	Heterodontus francisci	Aetobatus narinari

Sometimes logical organism groupings don't fit neatly into existing taxa. Taxonomists solve this be creating super and sub levels between the conventional taxa.

Six-Kingdom and Three-Domain Systems

Taxonomists differ somewhat about the highest life classifications, so that at present there is the *six-kingdom system* and the *three-domain system*. In the six-kingdom system, all life fits into the six broadest classifications: kingdoms Eubacteria, Archaebacteria, Protista, Fungi, Plante and Animalia. Some countries however, use a system of five classification domains: kingdom Animalia, kingdom Plantae, kingdom Fungi, kingdom Protista, and kingdom Prokaryota or Monera; a similar classification yet slightly different. The PADI Underwater Naturalist course focuses on Animalia because aquatic ecosystems tend to be animal dominated, though all kingdoms are vital and have pivotal roles in aquatic ecosystems.

Many taxonomists organize the kingdoms into three higher *domains* based on genetic and biochemical research: domains Archea, Bacteria and Eukarya. Kingdom Animalia is in domain Eukarya.

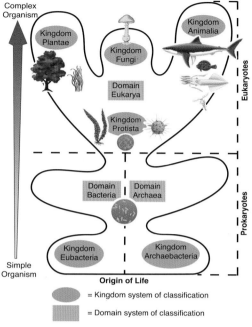

As early biologists learned more about the world around them, they developed a visual representation of how organisms fit with one another. This visual representation is often called the tree of life or taxa tree. This taxa tree illustration highlights not only the kingdom but also the domain classification systems. The bottom of the tree begins with the most simple of all life forms. Complex organisms are organized at the top of the tree.

Exercise 2 - The Linnaeus Classification System

1. Scientists classify organisms because
   - ☐ a. it helps identify an organism's relationship with other organisms.
   - ☐ b. it requires scientists to clearly identify key organism characteristics.
   - ☐ c. it helps avoid confusion about the organism in question.
   - ☐ d. All of the above.

2. _____ are grouped together in _____.
   - ☐ a. Species, classes
   - ☐ b. Genera, species
   - ☐ c. Orders, phyla
   - ☐ d. Families, orders.

3. An organism's scientific name represents the taxa
   - ☐ a. species and class.
   - ☐ b. genus and species.
   - ☐ c. family and order.
   - ☐ d. order and phylum.

4. Taxonomists classify organisms based on _____ and _____.
   - ☐ a. anatomical features, DNA
   - ☐ b. ecosystem, DNA
   - ☐ c. anatomical features, ecosystem
   - ☐ d. None of the above.

5. Taxonomists solve the problem of organisms that don't fit cleanly into defined taxa by
   - ☐ a. declassifying the organism.
   - ☐ b. creating higher or lower intermediate levels.
   - ☐ c. starting over with the entire kingdom's classification.
   - ☐ d. All of the above.

6. The three-domain system differs from the six-kingdom system because it does not use the kingdom classifications at all.
   - ☐ True   ☐ False

How'd you do?
1. d. *2.* d. *3.* b. *4.* a. *5.* b. *6.* False. *The three-domain system differs from the six-kingdom system by classifying the kingdoms within three domains.*

Overview of *Aquatic Life*

Biologists study organisms in several ways. One way is through taxonomy, which, as you just learned, examines the anatomy and DNA of organisms to find possible natural relationships with other organisms. They also study organisms within the context of their ecosystems, looking at the relationship between particular organisms and other organisms.

Considering that a dedicated researcher can spend an entire career studying a single family, or even a single species, it's easy to see that a comprehensive study of all aquatic organisms is clearly beyond the scope of this course. But, as a PADI Underwater Naturalist you should understand the broad characteristics of the taxa you'll find in the aquatic world, and you should be able to recognize basic relationships between organisms in their ecosystems. We'll start with a look at some basic characteristic groups, followed by a broad view of some phyla and classes and their aquatic representatives. Finally, we'll look at the two primary interrelationships between organisms of different species.

Life On An Ocean Planet,
Chapter Five.

Learn more...

Photosynthesizers

Organisms that photosynthesize – combine sunlight and carbon to create chemical energy – are the base of the food web in both aquatic and terrestrial environments. It is through these that sunlight powers almost all the life on earth; without these primary producers, earth's

Study Objectives

Underline/highlight the answers to these questions as you read:

1. What are the three types of aquatic photosynthesizers?

2. What is the difference between an invertebrate and a vertebrate?

3. What characterizes the aquatic animals in each major invertebrate and vertebrate phylum?

ecosystems would collapse, making these organisms vital to our continued survival. There are three primary types of aquatic photosynthesizers.

Phytoplankton. Phytoplankton are typically single celled microscopic organisms that live adrift in the surface layers of most bodies of water. They are the most important source of energy for the aquatic realm, to the degree that without them, there would be no life, as we know it in the ocean. Organisms ranging from microscopic animals to the largest baleen whales feed upon phytoplankton.

These organisms are also the world's primary source of oxygen.

Algae. Commonly called "seaweed," you find many algae types in both fresh and salt water. Although you may think of algae as plants, they're not actually plants because they lack true roots, stems, leaves and flowers. Some are single cell, microscopic organisms, whereas others like kelp are large, multicellular organisms with structures like holdfasts (root-like structures, but not true roots) and gas bladders that hold them erect.

The larger algae are grouped as red algae, brown algae and green algae. Algae reproduce by spores and the production of eggs and sperm. Although they're not food for as many organisms as are phytoplankton, many aquatic animals use algae as a food source.

Aquatic plants. Aquatic plants include eelgrass, surf grass, turtle grass and various species of mangrove trees, among others. Sometimes called "seaweed," this group includes true flowering plants that are typically found growing in sand bottoms in shallow water. Some species, such as sea grasses, live entirely underwater; others live partially submerged in wetlands where the aquatic and terrestrial worlds meet. Aquatic plants are a food source for many animals, but they're important for other reasons as well. Mangrove swamps, for example, usually live adjacent to offshore coral reefs. Mangroves are vital

Photograph © Mr. Ben Mieremet, Senior Advisor OSD, NOAA

Phytoplankton, algae and aquatic plants are the aquatic world's primary photosynthesizers. All are important because they convert sunlight energy into the chemical energy that fuels almost all life on earth. Some, such as mangroves shown here, also create environments that are important to aquatic world's health.

to coral health because they act as protective "nurseries" where juvenile species can grow until large enough to join the reef community, and because they absorb wave energy that would otherwise erode the coastline.

Aquatic Animals

As you already learned, most aquatic environments are animal dominated rather than plant dominated. Therefore, most of the organisms you'll observe as a PADI Underwater Naturalist will be animals.

There are several phyla in kingdom Animalia (the animal kingdom), and the following discussion looks at body plan and form, life history, feeding and defense tactics common to those with significant representatives in the aquatic world. The approach will be to go from the simplest organisms to the more complex, though again, this discussion isn't comprehensive.

The vast majority of phyla are groups of *invertebrates*, which are animals that have no backbones. All *vertebrates* (animals with backbones) are part of the phylum Chordata, but there are many different types of vertebrates. Therefore, we'll look at the next level, class, within Chordata and their representatives in the aquatic world.

Phylum Porifera (pronounced *pore-if-er-a*, meaning "pore-bearing"): Sponges

Body plan and form: Members of this phylum have a nonsymmetrical body that's perforated by pores and canals. These animals have soft tissue that's supported by small, needle-like structures called *spicules*, or by stingy threads. There is no identifiable organ system.

Life history: Sponges reproduce by eggs and sperm, and by budding. Budding is the process by which a piece of sponge breaks off and, after settling some place suitable, grows into a new sponge. Sponges release eggs and sperm may look like they're smoking, and a treat to see while you're diving.

Feeding and defense: Sponges feed by filtering plankton and organic material from the water. They draw in water through their external surface and expel it through one or more large openings that characterize sponges. Sponges defend themselves by being fibrous and unappetizing to most (but not all) potential predators, with a few species having stinging or toxic properties as well. Most sponges have tremendous regenerative abilities, and quickly close and regrow damaged areas.

Phylum Cnidaria (pronounced *nye-dar-ia*): Corals, anemones, jellyfish

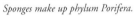

Sponges make up phylum Porifera.

Body plan and form: Cnidarians are radially symmetrical, meaning their bodies look like the spokes of a wheel. Some, like sea anemones, take a polyp form, where as others like the jellyfish have a medusa form. These animals have a single opening that serves as both mouth and anus for digestive tract. Tentacles with stinging cells ring the opening for capturing prey as well as for defense.

Life history: Cnidarians reproduce by budding and through fission (the animal divides in two, with each part growing into an adult). Some species also reproduce sexually, with males releasing sperm and females releasing the eggs into the water. The microscopic larvae that grow from fertilized eggs either settle and attach on the seafloor (polyp-forms including anemones and coral) or grow into adults medusa form (like jellyfish).

Feeding and defense: All cnidarians are carnivores that capture prey with their stinging tentacles. Smaller species feed on plankton, whereas large species like jellyfish may feed on fish.

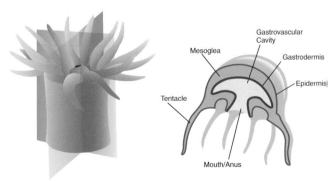

Cnidarians include sea anemones, corals and jellyfish, and have two basic body plans. These are the polyp form, which typically attached (anemones, coral), and the medusa form (jellyfish), which is typically free swimming.

Phylum Annelida (pronounced *an-ella-da*, meaning *ringed* for the rings that characterize their body segments): Segmented worms.

Annelids are bilaterally symmetrical (their bodies are symmetrical along either side of a line, like humans) and divided into regularly repeating segments. These worms have organ systems and have a specialized head and feeding parts. Two of the most common ones divers see are Christmas tree worms and fire worms.

Life history: Some annelids live attached to floor or reef in some kind of tube or burrow, while others crawl about. They reproduce by dividing, or sexually with sperm and eggs released into the water for external fertilization. The resulting microscopic larvae go through several stages before settling down to the sea floor as adults. Some species can reproduce through regeneration, in which a piece of an adult breaks off and grows into an adult.

Feeding and defense: Almost all annelids are predators. Attached tube-dwelling forms like the Christmas Tree Worm filter small planktonic prey from the water (the feathery bristles you see protruding from the burrow are the filters). Species that move about actively hunt for other worms, small shrimp, crabs and small snails. Some graze on sponges and corals. Tube-dwelling forms retreat into their tubes or burrows for defense, whereas mobile species use spines, jaws and their ability to burrow quickly.

Photograph © OAR/NURP

Caribbean tubeworms are tube-dwelling annelids. The large, feathery organs filter plankton from the water, with the rest of the worm hidden and protected by its burrow below.

Phylum Mollusca (pronounced *mole-us-ka*, meaning *head-foot*): Snails, slugs, clams, octopus and squid.

Body plan and form: All mollusks share the common characteristics of being bilaterally symmetrical, having a large, fleshy foot as a prominent part of their bodies, and a hard shell that is present as a single, spiral form (snails), a series of overlapping plates (chitons), or a symmetrical pair of shells (clams). Mollusks also have well developed organ systems.

Mollusks have five main body plans. These are: 1) snails and slugs, which have a large foot and mostly spiral shells, 2) chitons, which have a large foot and eight over-lapping plates as a shell, 3) clams and oysters, which have a large digging foot and a paired shell, 4) octopus and squid, in which the foot has developed into eight or more sucker-lined arms and the shell is greatly reduced or absent and 5) tusk shells, which have elongated tubular tapered shells that are open at both ends, with a conical foot at one end that protrudes and can be used only for burrowing.

Life history: The Life histories vary greatly for each of these five groups, but most mollusks use sexual reproduction. Some species do this by releasing eggs and sperm into the water where external fertilization occurs, where as others lay eggs fertilized internally through copulation. Some species, including octopus, brood (protect) internally fertilized eggs. Larvae resulting from any one of these methods become part of the plankton for a time before settling down to the seafloor to become adults.

Feeding and defense: With so much species diversity, mollusks have a broadly differing feeding and defense methods. Most snails graze on either plants or attached animals such as sponges and corals. Nearly all clams and their kin (oysters and scallops) filter feed on plankton, while octopus and squid are active predators of fish, crabs and clams. Defense mechanisms include shells, fleeing and the ability to change color (octopus).

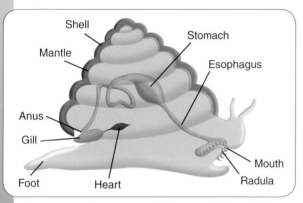

There are more than 100,000 mollusk species, which generally share these anatomical features, though some structures take different forms and may be greatly reduced or absent in some species.

Phylum Arthropoda (pronounced *are-throw-poe-da*, meaning *jointed foot*): Lobsters, crabs, hermit crabs, crayfish, shrimp and barnacles.

Body plan and form: All the aquatic members of this huge phylum (which includes insects) are in superclass Crustacea *(crust-a-see-a)*. All are *bilaterally symmetrical* and are covered with a hard outer body covering (made of *chitin* – pronounced *kie-tin*) that resembles jointed armor (thus the name *jointed foot*). There are two main body forms: the shrimp type and the crab type. The crab type is best described as the shrimp type with the tail tucked underneath the main body. Crustaceans have organ systems, including a simple circulatory system.

Life history: All crustaceans go through a series of stages (as many as 12) developing from tiny microscopic larvae into an adult. They reproduce sexually, usually involving copulation. Females may release thousands of fertilized eggs, though some species (such as lobsters) may carry them until they hatch. As crustaceans grow, they periodically molt (shed) their chitin shell, which doesn't grow, and a new one hardens around them. Most crustaceans have a mobile lifestyle, with barnacles a noted exception. Copepods are near-microscopic crustaceans that are important because they consume the smallest plankton. Larger organisms feed on the copepods, making copepods a crucial energy bridge that holds the upper and lower levels of the food web together.

Feeding and defense: Most crustaceans are scavengers that feed on almost any organic matter. Some are more specialized and feed only on plants, whereas others such as large crabs, are predators that prey on animals such as snails by crushing their shells with massive claws. Their primary defense is their chitin covering, well-developed sense organs and keeping a low profile. Species including crabs and lobsters also defend themselves with powerful claws.

Lobsters and crabs are two common crustaceans you're likely to see while diving.

Phylum Echinodermata (pronounced *e-kine-a-derm-a-ta*, meaning *spiny-skinned*): Sea stars, urchins, cucumbers, lilies, brittle stars and basket stars.

Body plan and form: There are four main classes (groups) within phylum Echinodermata, and they all live in the ocean. There are no freshwater species. They all are radially symmetrical as adults, but as larvae they are *bilaterally* symmetrical. All Echinoderms have *tube* feet, which are unique structures that help them move across the bottom. Most have some type of spines embedded in their tissues that provide structural support or, as in sea urchins, defense mechanisms.

Life history: Echinoderms primarily reproduce sexually, though some species can reproduce by regeneration. For example, if something breaks pieces off some sea stars, the sea star regrows the missing piece and the piece grows into a sea star. Males and females shed eggs and sperm into the water by the millions, with fertilization occurring externally in the water. The microscopic larvae go through a series of changes before they settle to the seafloor as adults.

Photograph © Bob Wohlers

Feeding and defense: Most Echinoderms are predators. Sea stars feed on clams and other slow-moving or attached prey. Sea urchins, however, are herbivores, grazing on marine plants and algae. This makes them particularly important in coral ecosystems because they control algae that compete with coral polyps. Sea cucumbers are either filter feeders or bottom scavengers. Most Echinoderms rely on their tough, spiny outer bodies for defense. The entire phylum exhibits great powers of regeneration, allowing most, but not all, species to survive significant damage by regenerating lost body portions.

Phylum Chordata, subphylum Urochordata (pronounced *you-orcore-data*): Sea squirts and salps.

Body plan and form: Subphylum Urochordata represents the members of phylum Chordata that are not vertebrates, with sea squirts the primary aquatic species from this subphylum. Salps are drifting colonial animals that feed on plankton. As larvae (juveniles), they resemble tiny tadpoles and have the beginnings of a backbone in their tails. As they develop, however, the tail disappears. Sea squirt larvae settle to the ocean floor, attach and take on the adult form, which is a nonsymmetrical sponge-like creature that looks like a sack with two projecting siphons. There are both individual and colonial forms of sea squirts, with the colonial forms looking even more like sponges. Salps live their entire lives drifting in the water column, much like a jellyfish.

Echinoderms include sea stars, brittle stars, sea urchins and sea cucumbers.

Photograph © Budd Riker

Sea squirts have similar lifestyle to sponges.

21

Life history: Sea squirts reproduce by budding or through the release of sperm into the water, which is taken in by the females to fertilize eggs. Eggs develop into tiny tadpole larvae, which eventually make their way to the seafloor where they attach, absorb the tail and take on the adult form.

Feeding and defense: All sea squirts are filter feeders as adults. They defend themselves primarily by having a tough tunic (outer covering).

Phylum Chordata, subphylum Vertebrata
(pronounced *ver-tay-bra-ta*): vertebrates.

All vertebrates, terrestrial and aquatic, make up subphylum Vertebrata. The following classes and other taxa are all within subphylum Vertebrata.

Class Chondrichthyes (pronounced *con-dry-ich-these* meaning *cartilage fish*): Sharks, rays and skates

Body plan and form: This group of fish is characterized by having an internal skeleton made of cartilage rather than true bone. They also have unique scales, gill structures and teeth that differ from other fish. There are two main body forms: skates and rays, which are flattened *dorsoventrally* (flattened on the top and bottom); and sharks, which have retained a streamlined, tubular body shape – i.e. shaped like a fish.

Life history: Rays and sharks reproduce sexually, have a low reproductive rate and slow growth. Most species fertilize through copulation and either release an egg case with several fertilized eggs (as in most skates and rays), or give birth to several live young (as in most sharks).

Feeding and defense: All skates, rays, and sharks are carnivores preying on everything from clams (rays) to other fish, seals and sea lions (great white sharks) and plankton (whale sharks). They locate their prey through extremely keen senses of smell, vision and the ability to detect vibrations in the water. Most members of this class have special organs that can sense the minute electrical field created by organisms; they use this ability for close range location. Most species capture and consume their prey by repeatedly biting with the well-armed mouth and jaws. The primary defense strategy for most species is fleeing or hiding, though a few species have specialized defense. Examples include the stingray, which has a defensive stinger in its tail, and the torpedo ray, which uses electric shock for hunting.

Photograph © Jurg Beeli

Photograph © Jurg Beeli

Class Chondrichthyes includes sharks, skates and rays.

Class Osteichthyes (pronounced *os-tie-ich-these* meaning *bony fish*): Bony fish

Body plan and form: The bony fish are characterized by having internal skeletons composed of true bone. All fish can be defined as aquatic, cold-blooded vertebrates that have gills throughout their life and limbs in the shape of fins (this definition includes sharks and rays, but sharks and rays do not have true bone skeletons). All fish are *bilaterally symmetrical* and have complete organ systems. The outer body covering is composed of scales (there are several types). Fish exhibit tremendous diversity in body shape, size and color.

Life history: All fish reproduce sexually. Some fertilize their eggs internally through copulation; others are *broadcast* spawners, releasing eggs and sperm into the water leading to external fertilization. Larval fish may or may not hatch out with a yolk sac attached. Most go through several developmental stages before reaching adulthood. Some fish, such as salmon, undergo long migrations from both fresh to salt and salt to fresh water as part of their reproduction process. Many species occupy different places in the ecosystem as they grow.

Feeding and defense: Given that there are more than 25,000 species in this class, it's not surprising that various fish feed on everything from scavenging, to plants to other fish. Head, jaw shape and dentition (the type, number and arrangement of a set of teeth) generally reflect the kinds of food a fish eats. Defense mechanisms also vary, and include camouflage, fleeing, spines, toxins, biting and flight (in flying fish). Schooling is also a defense mechanism that allows the group to unite efforts to detect and evade predators,

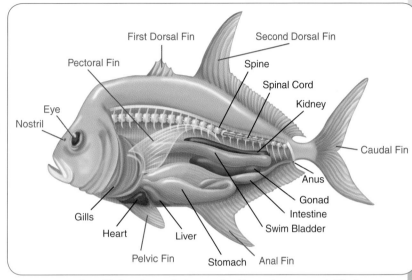

First Dorsal Fin · Second Dorsal Fin · Pectoral Fin · Spine · Spinal Cord · Kidney · Eye · Nostril · Caudal Fin · Anus · Gonad · Intestine · Swim Bladder · Gills · Heart · Liver · Anal Fin · Pelvic Fin · Stomach

Bony fish share the same basic external and internal anatomy, and differ from sharks and rays by having skeletons of true bone rather than cartilage.

and for the majority to escape as a predator focuses on an individual fish.

23

Class Reptilia (pronounced *rep-tile-i-a*), **order Chelonia**: Aquatic turtles

Body plan and form: Marine turtles vary from land turtles by having a streamlined shell and the inability to pull the head back into the shell. Also, their forelimbs are modified as rigid flippers and hind limbs as paddles. Some species of freshwater aquatic turtles show little difference from land turtles, whereas others have clear aquatic adaptations.

Life history: Aquatic turtles reproduce sexually. Internal fertilization occurs when males copulate with females. Marine female turtles leave the water, usually at night, to dig a nest on a beach, deposit several hundred leathery eggs and return to the sea. Several weeks later, the eggs hatch and the young return to the sea. Adult marine turtles make long migrations to return to the exact beach where they were born to lay their eggs.

Feeding and defense: Aquatic turtles feed on a variety of organisms and plants. Marine turtles feed on jellyfish and even hard corals, which they bite off with their hard beaks. Freshwater turtles feed on fish and other animals, and some species also eat plants. Turtles defend themselves with their hard shells, by escaping detection, by fleeing and by biting. Some freshwater species of snapping turtles have an especially powerful and tenacious bite.

The green sea turtle is a typical marine turtle with adaptations including forelimbs modified as flippers for aquatic living.

The greatest predation of sea turtles occurs when the small young hatchlings leave the beach nest and race to the water. They're very exposed to predators such as birds, crabs and shore mammals, which prey on the young. More young turtles evade predation if they hatch at night because the darkness helps conceal them as they dash to the water.

Class Reptilia, other orders: Crocodiles, alligators, snakes

Body plan and form: Body plans and forms vary in class Reptilia, but most fully aquatic reptiles are equipped with adaptations, such as specially flattened tails for swimming. You find this in crocodiles, alligators and sea snakes. Some species have no obvious adaptations to aquatic life, yet swim and function well in water, and may spend most of their lives in or near water. Freshwater snakes are common examples of this.

Life history: Reproduction is sexual and fertilization is internal. Crocodiles and alligators lay eggs in nests of decaying vegetation. Sea snakes retain the eggs within their bodies. The eggs hatch internally and the snakes give birth to live young. Most freshwater snakes lay eggs in nests.

Feeding and defense: Crocodiles, alligators and snakes are predators that feed on fish and other animals. All bite defensively. Sea snakes and some species of freshwater snakes are venomous.

Most fully aquatic reptiles have adaptations to living the water which commonly include a flattened tail for swimming.

Class Mammalia, order Sirenia (pronounced *sie-ree-nee-a*): Manatees

Body plan and form: Manatees are mammals, which mean they are warm-blooded, breathe air, have hair, bear live young, and suckle their young (some mammals lack hair and some lay eggs). Manatees are large (up to 4 metres / 12 feet long), have small eyes, no hind limbs (replaced by a single large paddle) and paddle-like flippers as forelimbs.

Life history: Like all mammals, manatees reproduce sexually, copulating to ensure internal fertilization. They usually give birth to a single calf.

Feeding and defense: Manatees are exclusively herbivorous and feed on aquatic plants such as water hyacinth. Their large size is their primary defense, as well as simply living in habitats where few large predators exist (mangrove swamps and shallow inland waterways). Historically, humans have been one of their primary predators, though today they are endangered, threatened primarily by the loss of habitat and injury by watercraft.

Manatees are large, herbivorous marine mammals.

Class Mammalia, order Pinnipedia (pronounced *pin-nee-pay-dia*): seals, sea lions and walrus

Body plan and form: Pinnipeds all share a sleek, elongated and streamlined body that's clearly adapted to aquatic life, but also to life out of but near the water. Seals, sea lions and walrus differ in key anatomical details. Seals have no earflaps and their hind limbs point backwards, whereas sea lions have external ear flaps and their rear hind limbs can rotate forward, which gives them more mobility out of water. Walrus have no earflaps, yet can rotate their hind limbs forward like sea lions.

Life history: Seals, sea lions and walrus reproduce sexually. Internal fertilization occurs through copulation. Most species are social animals that live in large herds dominated by one or a few larger, older males.

Feeding and defense: Pinnipeds are predators that eat primarily fish. Most species are fast and agile, so their primary defense is fleeing, which can include into the water to escape threats on land, or from the water to escape threats in the sea. Sea lions and seals are prey for great white sharks and orcas, and part of their defense strategy includes group living. Groups provide many individuals to detect a threat, and allow most animals to escape at the cost of a single member.

Pinnipeds are adapted to an aquatic life that includes periods out of, but near water.

Class Mammalia, order Cetacea (pronounced *see-tay-see-a*): Dolphins, porpoises and whales

Body plan and form: Mammals in order Cetacea breathe through a blowhole on the tops of their heads. They're characterized by having a fish-shaped body and no hind limbs. Instead, they have a broad, flattened fluke (tail) used for swimming, and their forelimbs are stiff flippers. They are essentially hairless and have blubber (thick fat layers) to insulate them from the cold.

Life history: Dolphins, whales and porpoises reproduce sexually through internal fertilization by copulation. Females typically birth a single calf after a long gestation period (11 months for most dolphins). There is a strong bond between the cow and the calf. Most dolphins, whales and porpoises form small to large (several hundred) social groups called pods. Depending upon the species, pods hunt, nurture young and defend each other together.

Feeding and defense:
Dolphins, porpoises and many whales feed primarily on squid and fish, which they catch with their mouths. Baleen whales are the largest animals on earth, and feed on plankton by filtering it from the water in

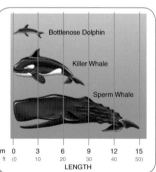

large volumes. Taking energy directly from the base of the food web allows them to attain their great size.

Some species hunt collectively, including orcas, which may unite to feed on larger whales. Cetaceans defend themselves by schooling and their ability to travel at high speeds. They also detect prey or potential danger at a distance with *echolocation*. Cetaceans emit high-energy sound waves that echo off objects; special organs allow these animals to determine size, movement, shape and distance of objects based on the echoes.

Exercise 3 - Overview of Aquatic Life

1. The three types of aquatic photosynthesizers include (check all that apply):
   - ☐ a. phytoplankton.
   - ☐ b. chemosynthetic bacteria.
   - ☐ c. algae.
   - ☐ d. aquatic plants.

2. A _____ is an animal with a backbone; a _____ is an animal without a backbone.
   - ☐ a. vertebrate, echinoderm
   - ☐ b. invertebrate, echinoderm
   - ☐ c. invertebrate, vertebrate
   - ☐ d. vertebrate, invertebrate

3. Species in phylum Porifera include (check all that apply)
   - ☐ a. sponges.
   - ☐ b. bony fish.
   - ☐ c. sea stars.
   - ☐ d. sea urchins.

4. Invertebrates that are bilaterally symmetrical, have a large, fleshy foot as a prominent body part, and either a hard shell, overlapping plates or a pair of symmetrical shells would be in
   - ☐ a. phylum Annelida.
   - ☐ b. phylum Mollusca.
   - ☐ c. phylum Arthropoda.
   - ☐ d. subphylum Urochordata.

How'd you do?
1. a, c, d. **2.** *d.* **3.** *a.* **4.** *b.*

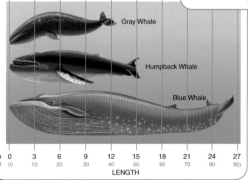

Cetaceans include dolphins, porpoises and whales. Baleen whales feed directly from the base of the food web and are the largest animals on earth.

Aquatic Organisms:
Myths and Human Misperceptions

Throughout recorded history, human perceptions of the aquatic world and its inhabitants have shaped how we interact with it and them. At one time, humans had very inaccurate ideas about most aquatic creatures' behaviors and physiology, leading to many misconceptions. For example, sailors viewed large creatures as monsters to fear, regardless of facts. By the mid 19th century, however, maritime experience had set aside many of the fears, and with the rise of industry, society saw the ocean as limitless resources to exploit. This perception continued well into the 20th century.

By the 1950s, scientists and naturalists were beginning to realize that we can harm the aquatic world significantly. Today we realize that the seas are not limitless, and that not only can we hurt them, but that we've essentially destroyed large areas. The public in modern society knows a lot more about aquatic life than in the past, thanks largely to the rise of scuba diving, underwater imaging and modern media.

Perhaps surprisingly, then, many misperceptions and myths remain today – even among divers. Some of these come from inaccurate representations in the media, but others arise out of our normal mental processes. One way our minds try to handle unfamiliar situations is by comparing them to familiar ones. For example, you

Study Objectives

Underline/highlight the answers to these questions as you read:

1. What does the label *hazardous* mean when applied to an organism?

2. What is the most common cause of aquatic animal "attacks"?

3. What is the difference between an *offensive* and a *defensive* action by an organism?

4. What is an accurate and objective view of hazardous aquatic animal "attacks"?

5. What are four misperceptions people may have about aquatic organisms?

may commonly hear divers say that sea lions remind them of curious, friendly dogs. But, the reality is that sea lions aren't like dogs at all (so don't try to pet one!). Another common example is that to the uninformed, based on terrestrial comparisons hard coral appears to be a nearly indestructible, non-living rock rather than the fragile colony of organisms that it actually is.

As a PADI Underwater Naturalist, you need to learn to recognize how the way you think can lead to misconceptions about aquatic life, as well as common beliefs that aren't true, and replace these with valid perceptions. Only then can you see aquatic creatures for what they really are, and understand their place in the ecosystem.

Potentially Hazardous Aquatic Animals

While humans have become the dominant species in most terrestrial environments, the same isn't true in aquatic environments. You don't have to reasonably fear a wild animal attack while walking around a coastal city like San

Francisco in the USA, Durban in South Africa or Naples in Italy, but enter the water and within sight of the buildings, traffic and human-dominance, you're open to an encounter with hazardous aquatic animals. Underwater environments adjacent to human-dominated areas are largely as wild as wildness in the untouched Australian outback, the large African reserves or remote Alaska, and humans are comparably vulnerable.

Attacks by large aquatic animals like sharks are rare, but feared because we perceive little or no control over them. Their rarity makes these events newsworthy, so that news media make them very public and conspicuous when they occur, reinforcing the horror and lack of control we perceive. It's no wonder that many myths and misconceptions relate to potentially hazardous aquatic animals.

What is "hazardous"? As a PADI Underwater Naturalist, it's important to view all aquatic life in context of their roles in their ecosystems, and this includes potentially hazardous organisms. All organisms are integral parts of their ecosystems and play a part in maintaining the system's health. Sharks, for example, are predators that keep fish and mammal populations in check and thereby help maintain the stability of food webs. Sea urchins feed on algae that would otherwise overrun coral reefs.

The label *hazardous* simply means that the organism in question can cause injury to human beings. It's not a value judgment, nor does it mean the organism is good or bad. Rather, it's an alert to you and others to use caution when you encounter or may encounter these species. An organism's characteristics relate entirely to its survival needs, so it's important to set aside feelings about its worth that arise from its ability or inability to harm a person. It is no more or less important to the ecosystem just because it is potentially hazardous in some way.

Attacks. Animals that are capable of "attacks" make up comparatively few of all potentially hazardous aquatic organisms. Often, we think of organisms that can attack as those that we can interpret as having intent or malice. These are typically animals with obvious eyes and mobility such as sharks, eels, snakes, orca, crocodiles, etc. A Portuguese man-o-war is potentially hazardous and can cause life-threatening stings, but no one would reasonably say it "attacks" if an unfortunate person accidentally swims into its tentacles.

It's important to recognize that "attacks" by potentially hazardous organisms (terrestrial or aquatic) result from instinctive behaviors. There is no malice or vengeance –those are exclusively human qualities.

When we think of "attacks" by potentially hazardous aquatic animals, we normally think of those that move with intent, have obvious eyes and are mobile. It's important to realize that virtually all "attacks" result from defensive or feeding behavior, and that animals never attack out of malice.

The most common cause of "attacks" is defensive behavior on the part of an animal. If you reach into a hole inhabited by a moray eel, there's a good chance you'll get bitten. The moray bites believing it has to defend itself. You wouldn't think of a sea urchin as "attacking" if you step on one, but it's important to recognize that getting spines in your feet results from exactly the same cause – the way a sea urchin defends itself.

Offensive and Defensive Actions. Although most injuries to humans result from defensive actions by organisms, some result from offensive actions. An *offensive action* is one in which the organism initiates the action. Typically, these are linked to feeding behavior, and based on instinct, not malice.

Humans aren't natural prey for any aquatic animals (aquatic ecosystems are not our natural habitat), so offensive actions result from mistaken perceptions by the organism. That is, the human resembles food in some way. One example is that eels accustomed to being hand fed may bite a diver's extended hand if it mistakes the hand for food. Another example, surfers paddling on a small surfboard resemble seals, great white sharks natural prey. Some scientists think that such a mistake may account for some attacks on surfers in areas where great whites feed or breed.

A *defensive action* is one in which the organism responses to defend itself, its mate, young or territory. This clearly pertains to sedentary organisms that sting to defend themselves like fire coral, sea urchins or scorpion fish. Mobile organisms that defend themselves by biting are those that may be associated with "attacks," but bites result from the same thing: an organism defending itself.

Therefore, an objective view of hazardous aquatic animal "attacks" is that such animal attacks are a response to human behaviors that cause animals to perceive the human as a food source or as a threat. This means that you can reduce the risk of aquatic injuries by taking the following steps.

An objective view of hazardous aquatic animal "attacks" is that such animal attacks are a response to human behaviors that cause animals to perceive the human as a food source or as a threat.

1. *Learn to recognize potentially hazardous aquatic life on sight.* As a diver, it's your responsibility to be aware of local creatures that may be hazardous, whether it's a stingray you might step on, fire coral you may bump up against, or large predatory types of shark. Local divers and a local PADI operation can brief you when you visit an unfamiliar area, and you can usually find what you need to know online as well.

2. *Understand the nature of the hazard and the potential severity.* A sea urchin is only a hazard if you put your hand or foot on it, and even if you do, while it's painful, it's not deadly or life threatening. On the other hand, snorkeling in a black wet suit in areas frequented by sea lions may make you appear to be prey to a great white shark. In this case, the hazard is much greater (the shark is definitely faster than you are) and can be deadly.

3. *Modify your behavior to avoid and substantially reduce the risk so that you don't trigger a defensive or unintentional offensive (feeding) behavior.* This is typically common sense, such as watching where you step or touch to avoid accidentally touching sea urchins and wearing gloves and thick-soled wet suit boots. Similarly, you may avoid snorkeling in a black wet suit in areas where great whites feed on sea lions. Dive briefings sometimes cover unusual steps you may need to take based on local species. When night diving in the Caribbean, for example, it is common to purge your regulator and

send up a large air burst before ascending, and to do so looking up and around very carefully. This is because dive lights attract some species of stinging jellyfish. Similarly, it's a good idea to wear a full exposure suit (at least a body suit) to reduce the risk of being stung.

4. *With respect to mobile, higher intelligence animals, it's what the organism perceives that determines behavior.* It doesn't matter what you intend. Therefore, to reduce potential risk, you need to take actions based on possible perceptions an organism may have. As mentioned, if great white sharks feed in an area, you need to avoid dressing and swimming in a way that may cause it to perceive you as food. It's predictable that a sting ray will perceive being stepped on as an attack and respond by stinging, so be cautious about where you step while walking on sandy bottoms where sting rays may be found.

Misperceptions and Myths about Aquatic Organisms

As a naturalist, it is important that you have an accurate perception of the natural world. A good place to start is to clarify common misperceptions and myths about aquatic organisms. There are four broad categories of these:

1. **Aquatic organisms as dangerous and harmful.** Obviously there are potentially hazardous organisms as we discussed in the previous section. Uninformed or misinformed people may view sharks or other species that can harm humans as unrealistically dangerous or bad, or they may have an unspecified fear, such as there are "things" in the lake that will get you. Lack of information, misinformation or inaccurate associations can cause people to perceive threats when none exist, such as thinking morays have a poisonous bite because they have snake-like bodies. Until recently, people believed manta

Reduce your potential risk by taking actions based on perceptions an organism may have. For example, if in an area where great white sharks feed, avoid dressing and swimming in a way that may cause a great white shark to mistake you for a sea lion (its prey).

rays are dangerous (they were even called "devil rays") primarily because they are large and (to the uninformed) fearsome looking.

Perceptions about "danger" sometimes grow due to exaggeration during the excitement of retelling a story, especially if it gets passed from one person to another, much as urban legends do. An incident about an inquisitive two metre/six foot shark evolves into narrowly escaping a blood-thirsty assault by a 5 metre/15 foot beast as the tale passes from one yarn spinner to the next.

Misunderstandings also feed inaccuracies. For example, a shark landed by an angler will flop on deck and gasp. If it happens to writhe toward the angler while opening and closing its jaws, the story becomes "It came after me in the boat!" because the person doesn't realize the movement was coincidence. Or, someone mistakes a moray eel opening and closing its mouth for breathing as an expression of aggression.

While modern media have done a lot to make us better informed about the ocean, they are still a source of inaccurate information. Portrayals in cinema and television continue to play up and perpetuate myths about potentially hazardous animals for entertainment purposes.

As you already learned, while some organisms can be potentially hazardous, we are the ones who can cause a dangerous situation by intentionally or unintentionally disregarding the behaviors and mechanisms that can lead to injury.

See *Protect the Sharks* and *Attacking the Shark Myth* at www.projectaware.org

2. **As harmless animals similar to domestic or friendly terrestrial animals.** Instead of viewing aquatic animals as unrealistically dangerous, people may misperceive them as being unrealistically harmless. Uninformed people may have both misperceptions, believing some animals to be more dangerous than they are, and others to be less dangerous than they really are.

It's a normal mental mechanism to deal with something you don't know by drawing comparisons with something you do know. With respect to wild organisms, however, be wary and interact with them based on education and observations rather than based on what you might expect from domesticated animals.

While you can learn many of the behaviors you expect from different animals, the accurate view is that animals in the wild are still unpredictable, and you should treat them that way. This is especially true of higher order animals that have two eyes and exhibit complete behaviors to which you may relate, perhaps comparing to a dog or cat. Unfortunately, that can lead to misunderstandings, and at worst, lead to injuries if you fail to recognize potential defensive or feeding behavior triggers. If, after seeing a trainer pet a sea lion at a zoo you attempted to pet a wild one, you may end up severely bitten.

It's a normal mental mechanism to deal with something you don't know by drawing comparisons with something you do know. With respect to wild animals, aquatic and terrestrial for that matter, we need to be wary and interact with them based on education and observations rather than based on what we might expect from domesticated animals.

3. **As non-living, inanimate objects.** It's possible to treat living things as though they are not alive, and in fact, we do it all the time. As an example, many people would think nothing of driving a nail into a living tree to hang a clothesline. Although they know intellectually that the tree is alive, it doesn't show pain or react to the injury, so it is inanimate for practical purposes.

Similarly, animals that lack eyes and mobility underwater are easy to perceive as inanimate, either psychologically or ignorantly. These include coral, sea urchins, sea fans, sea stars, sea cucumbers and sponges. To the uninformed, these may not seem to be animals, and in the cases of coral and sea fans, they may not even seem to be alive at all. Alternatively, sometimes divers treat even very animate living things as inanimate

due to emotional detachment, such as playing with an inflated puffer fish as though it were a balloon instead of a living creature.

It's easy to perceive organisms that lack eyes, mobility and complex behaviors as less valuable, less important or, in a sense, less alive. As an underwater naturalist, however, you need to realize that an organism's value in an ecosystem doesn't depend upon its behaviors or complexity, and there are thousands of examples. Corals are the basis for some of the most biologically productive ecosystems on earth. The ocean food web relies on single cell, microscopic primary producers to bring in energy from the sun, and at the same time, provide a major portion of the oxygen we breathe. Bacteria and other microorganisms break down complex, toxic organic waste compounds into non-toxic compounds that other organisms grow on. It turns out that some of the least animal-like animals are the most important to the global ecosystem.

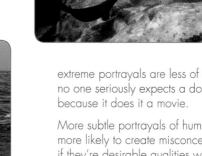

that have nothing to do with the question. While you probably recognize these stunts for what they are, they may contribute to expecting human qualities on an unconscious, emotional level.

Television and cinema have portrayed many different types of animals with having human or near human qualities, sometimes in a context that one can mistakenly take as fact. Ironically,

extreme portrayals are less of a problem because no one seriously expects a dog or cat to talk just because it does it a movie.

More subtle portrayals of human characteristics are more likely to create misconceptions, especially if they're desirable qualities we would like to believe the animal has. The 1960s US television show *Flipper*, for example, portrayed a dolphin as a loyal and intelligent creature that summoned aid, solved problems and otherwise aided human companions in one adventure after another. This played upon and reinforced a popular view of dolphins as gentle, friendly and intelligent, but ignored the reality that dolphins don't really recognize when humans are in trouble, and even if they did, they wouldn't care.

The fact that some animals *do* exhibit behaviors that we can relate to as humans also adds to the problem. Dolphins, whales and some fish species protect their young, just as we do. Several fish and shark species defend territory, just as we do.

4. **As having human characteristics.**
   Anthropomorphism, or attributing human characteristics to animals because they exhibit complex, human like behavior, is on the other end of the misperception spectrum. Some attributions may come from attempts to entertain by having trained animals behave or appear human-like, such as having dolphins wear sunglasses or chimpanzees wear clothes. Trained animals may nod "yes" or "no" to questions based on signals by the trainer

The important point, though, is that sharing basic behaviors with humans doesn't mean having human qualities. As a clear example of the difference, a single cell amoeba eats to sustain itself, just like humans do – but that hardly gives it human qualities.

The problem with portraying animals as having human qualities is that it impedes recognizing them for what they really are. You may end up making value judgments based on an organism's perceived humanity (or lack of it), instead of its role and place in the ecosystem. As a PADI Underwater Naturalist, it's important to see and value organisms for what they are, not for what we might want them to be.

The fact that some animals do exhibit behaviors that we can relate to as humans may contribute to perceiving them as having human characteristics. Dolphins, whales and some fish species protect their young, just as we do. However, sharing basic behaviors with humans doesn't mean having human qualities.

Exercise 4 – Aquatic organisms: Myths and human misperceptions

1. When applied to an aquatic organism, the label "hazardous" means
   - ☐ a. it is a predator that specifically seeks out divers as prey.
   - ☐ b. the organism has caused injury to human beings.
   - ☐ c. the organism is evil.
   - ☐ d. All of the above.

2. The most common cause of animal "attacks" is
   - ☐ a. defensive behavior on the part of the animal.
   - ☐ b. revenge behavior on the part of the animal.
   - ☐ c. spawning behavior on the part of the animal.
   - ☐ d. a profound dislike of divers.

3. A _____ action is one in which the organism initiates the action. It is typically linked to _____ behavior.
   - ☐ a. defensive; mating
   - ☐ b. defensive; feeding
   - ☐ c. offensive; mating
   - ☐ d. offensive; feeding

4. An accurate (objective) view of aquatic animal "attacks" is that they result from human behaviors that cause animals to perceive the human as a food source or a threat to it, a mate, young or territory.
   - ☐ True   ☐ False

5. Inaccurate ways people may perceive aquatic organisms include (check all that apply):
   - ☐ a. as dangerous and harmful.
   - ☐ b. as harmless animals similar to domestic animals.
   - ☐ c. as having a specific role in its ecosystem.
   - ☐ d. as having human characteristics.

How'd you do?
1. b. *2.* a. *3.* d. *4.* True. *5.* a, b, d.

Human Interactions with *Aquatic Life*

No matter how quietly, calmly and benignly you dive, you can't enter the underwater world without interacting with it. Compared to most organisms, you're big and therefore, a potential threat from the perspective of many of them. Furthermore, you make sounds, emit vibrations and even release chemicals that organisms can detect. This doesn't differ at all from terrestrial environments. If you go into a woods, desert or highland, the natural inhabitants will hear, see and smell you. If you're in a natural environment, wet or dry, you're interacting with it.

Passive and Active Interactions

Consider the activities you could carry out as a diver: sightseeing, photography, videography, searching for wrecks, collecting tropical fish, scientific research, night diving, deep diving, recovery, spearfishing, shell collecting, fish feeding, boat repair and so on. You can classify each of these as *passive* interaction, *active* interaction or "it depends."

Passive interactions are those that involve only observing aquatic life and doing so in a way that minimizes disrupting its natural behavior. This means, for example, you do your best to avoid threatening fish, even inadvertently, or frightening tube worms with your shadow or vibrations.

Although passive interaction primarily means just watching, it's also the best way to get to see some of nature's most interesting animals and their behaviors. When animals don't perceive you as a threat, they ignore you and go about their lives as if you weren't there. Creatures warily come out of hiding. You'll see fish and other animals feed, defend territory or breed just as they would if you weren't there.

Study Objectives

Underline/highlight the answers to these questions as you read:

1. How do you passively interact with aquatic organisms?
2. Can you responsibly touch or handle aquatic life?
3. Why should you not ride aquatic animals?
4. Can you hunt or take of aquatic life responsibly?
5. Why should divers avoid feeding aquatic animals and fish?
6. What diving techniques should you use to preserve bottom dwelling organisms and to minimize disturbing aquatic life?

Passive interaction involves observing aquatic organisms in a way that minimizes disrupting their natural behaviors.

Active interactions are those that directly affect aquatic organisms and affect their natural behaviors. You may be actively interacting intentionally, or unintentionally, as a byproduct of something else you're doing. An unambiguous example of intentional active interaction is spearfishing. An example of unintentional active interaction could be disturbing bottom sediments and the organisms that live in them while recovering an object from the bottom. While you may only have been interested in recovering an object and have never intended to disturb the organisms, by removing the object you have caused the disturbance.

It's important to realize that active interactions aren't necessarily detrimental in any significant way. Active interactions that have little or no long-term effect aren't likely to be an issue. This is fortunate because many things we do as divers wouldn't be possible without some degree of active interaction. Using a strobe when you take a photo may be an active interaction if it startles a fish, for instance, but you wouldn't expect it to have a lasting effect. Similarly, a researcher may have to touch or move organisms to survey them, but avoids any lasting effects by replacing them exactly where they were. Neither of these examples would be considered irresponsible or unreasonable, even though they're active interactions.

"It depends" interactions are those that may be passive, clearly active or in between depending upon how you conduct them. For example, you can shoot underwater photos or video in a manner that's relatively passive, or in ways that significantly disrupt natural behaviors. Specialties like night diving and deep diving fall in the same category – how you conduct yourself during a night or deep dive determines whether your actions are passive or active.

Passive Observations. Let's look at observations of aquatic life you can make as an underwater naturalist interacting passively, or actively with no long term effect.

The first is observations of an individual animal. You may watch it move, feed, build a nest or some other behavior. As a naturalist, note both how the animal's behaviors differ from and are the same as other organisms'. A second type observation is of a group of the same species. You may note behaviors like schooling, group movement, defending territory, courtship/mating rituals and other behaviors. Again, watch for how behaviors are unique to that group, and behaviors it shares with other groups.

A third type observation is of two or more organisms of different species interacting. These behaviors may include forms of symbiosis, predator-prey behaviors and defending territory.

A fourth observation is of active interactions between a diver and organisms. These may include fish defending its territory from you, fleeing a perceived threat, feeding on debris from a disturbed bottom and so on. Depending where you are, you may observe divers hunting or taking sea life in some other way; if this happens, observe the alarm and other reactions of organisms in the area as divers take or spear others.

35

Part of your skills as a diver in general, but as a PADI Underwater Naturalist in particular, necessarily includes diving in ways that are as unobtrusive as possible. This includes using streamlined, environmentally friendly techniques, but also behaviors and body positioning. Stay neutrally buoyant and avoid abrupt, jerky movements, which fish and other aquatic life perceive as threats. Move slowly, gently and smoothly.

Try to observe creatures from well above or below their level, so you seem less like a predator. Fish and other complex organisms may flee or take cover if you look directly at them or if you are too close because you're exhibiting predator behavior. Back off, change level and align your body so it's not pointed straight at the animals you're observing. It may even help to avoid staring or looking directly at some species that instinctively pay attention to the eyes of potential predators.

If you see fish or other organisms flee from you, you're not interacting passively, even if you're trying to – you'll improve with practice. You'll also notice that it's easier to swim around organisms without disturbing them in protected areas frequented by divers. In these areas, fish in particular become used to divers and learn that they aren't a threat.

As a PADI Underwater Naturalist, you want to move about as unobtrusively as possible, not disrupting normal wildlife behaviors. In protected areas frequented by divers, you may find this easier because fish and other wildlife become used to divers and learn they're not a threat.

Touching and Handling Wildlife

Touching and handling wildlife is obviously not passive interaction, no matter how gentle and careful you are. Nonetheless, you can do it responsibly at times, provided you don't cause a significant disruption to the organism's normal behavior.

Handling wildlife should only be done if you have the experience or education needed to do so safely for both *you and the organism*. You obviously can't touch or handle many animals safely because they bite or sting. Likewise, your touch is deadly or injurious to many organisms. This is particularly true of fish, which have mucus coatings that protect them from parasites and infection. Even gentle attempts at handling a fish can remove this coating and make it vulnerable. Therefore, before you consider handling any living organism, you need to ask, "Can this hurt it?" and "Can this hurt me?" and be *certain* that the answer to both is "no."

Next, ask yourself what the benefit would be. Touching or handling an organism should only take place if doing so provides a meaningful learning experience, such as in teaching a class or conducting research, and only if it doesn't compromise the organism's well being. If there's no meaningful benefit, then leave organisms where they are, as undisturbed as possible as they go about playing their mysterious roles in the ecosystem.

One form of touching that is *never* appropriate in the wild is riding aquatic animals. You may have seen this on television or in the movies, particularly during the 1960s and 1970s. As our understanding has grown since then, we've learned that this isn't an acceptable practice.

There are *no* circumstances in which riding wild aquatic animals benefits it. In fact, in many cases, riding an aquatic animal can harm it directly or indirectly. Your touch can cause injuries directly, or remove protective barriers that protect the animal from infection and parasites. In the case of air breathing animals, riding it can drown it by holding it down longer than it can

hold its breath. This is especially true of turtles, which become frightened and consume their oxygen faster while struggling to escape. Attempts to ride, at the very least, usually scare off the animal, cutting short your opportunity to enjoy watching it.

Another reason riding aquatic animals is a bad idea is that they can hurt you. Many will react defensively with biting or thrashing. And, a sea turtle bite, as an example, is not a minor injury. Even seemingly gentle animals, like whale sharks and whales, may react defensively, or simply tow you fast enough to cause injury if you collide with something.

There are no circumstances in which riding an aquatic animal benefits it, and doing so may result in injury to you, the animal or both.

Hunting and Taking of Aquatic Organisms

Humans are not aquatic animals, but we have always depended on the oceans for food. Over most of earth's history, when the human population was relatively small and the oceans so vast, our consumption has had little effect on the aquatic world. However, with a population boom and technical advances, this has changed substantially since the late 19th century.

One thing we do know is that predation by humans isn't necessary for the health of aquatic ecosystems. We're not, like sharks, the apex ocean predators that are necessary for the health of the marine ecosystems and there's no benefit to the environment from human consumption of aquatic organisms. In marine preserves that prohibit extractive activities, such as fishing, spearfishing, or collecting, aquatic organisms tend to flourish and their numbers and sizes are sometimes order of magnitudes larger than in adjacent, unprotected areas.

Aquatic organisms today are under tremendous pressure from extractive activities and environmental degradation we have caused. Many species, once thought to be limitless, are now commercially, and possibly, ecologically extinct. We're taking from the oceans at a rate that exceeds most species' ability to survive and function. Aquatic life and ocean health are subject to further human effects such as overfishing, pollution, runoff, coastal development, etc.

Compared to many ways humans take from the sea for commercial purposes, the taking of fish and organisms for sport or collections is minor on the global scale. However, there's more to it than a numbers game. Recreational take of aquatic organisms can affect species substantially. And, as some of the most visible ambassadors for the underwater world, divers in particular, are very obvious in their practices. Like it or not, as a diver – especially as a PADI Underwater Naturalist – you set an example.

If you choose to engage in any form of taking aquatic life, always follow all local laws, and *follow them conservatively*. Game laws, for example, regulate sizes, seasons, genders, species and quantities of organisms that can be taken with the goal of assuring their availability now and in the future. However, these laws are often a compromise between those seeking to protect a species and those who want to take it, meaning that the limits may be more liberal than what would be best for the species. Therefore, the best practice is to take no more than you will use personally, and to take less than allowed by law. Remember that since scuba diving is generally considered a non-extractive activity, many popular diving areas prohibit all forms of hunting and taking.

When in doubt, do without. You won't starve if you leave an organism in the environment, and the environment will be better off. Be sure to measure any potential game before taking it or otherwise disrupting its normal behavior. Err on the side of caution – if you're not sure if it's legal or illegal to take any organism, then assume it's illegal and leave it alone.

Remember that capturing animals for an aquarium, for a personal shell collection or any other purpose is like hunting underwater; you must be responsible and follow all laws. Better yet, purchase the organisms from licensed dealers who only obtain their stock through legal, responsible methods of collection or breeding. The same applies to your seafood choices: buy your seafood only from responsible sources, and don't buy species that are at risk due to commercial pressure.

 Visit www.projectaware.org to download a copy of your local seafood buying guide.

The bottom line is to be conservative. Removing any organism from the environment affects the local ecosystem, even if the effects aren't immediately obvious. The environment will *always* be better off if you don't take an organism.

Sustainable Fisheries: 10 Things You Can Do to Help

1. Make informed decisions while selecting seafood. Support fisheries that are better for the environment and relieve pressure on those that aren't doing as well. Many organizations inform consumers about which seafood to select and which to avoid to reduce overfishing and damage to the underwater environment.

2. When buying seafood, look for eco-labels such as Dolphin Friendly or Marine Stewardship Council. The Marine Stewardship Council (MSC) has developed an environmental standard for sustainable and well-managed fisheries. This designation rewards environmentally responsible fishery management practices. The label ensures consumers that the product has not contributed to overfishing. For an international directory of MSC certified fisheries, visit msc.org.

3. Ask your local supermarkets and restaurants if they stock seafood with sustainable labels. If not or they don't know, encourage them to add sustainable species to their product line. Your consumer power can influence local businesses.

4. Don't assume that farmed seafood is always an environmentally friendly alternative. Depending on the species, farms can introduce or increase waste, toxins, disease and chemicals into the natural environment. Carnivorous species like salmon and shrimp require an unsustainable amount of wild caught fish to reach marketable size. This means that the increase in farmed carnivorous fish still put pressure on fished species as they are caught to produce feed. For example, to produce .5 kg/1 lb of farmed salmon requires from 1-2 kg/2-5 lbs of ocean fish as food. By knowing your seafood source, you can use sustainable seafood guides and eco-labels to guide your decisions.

(continued...)

Sustainable Fisheries: 10 Things You Can Do to Help (...continued)

5. Eat lower down on the food chain. Fish species that are higher on the food chain such as tuna, swordfish and shark, tend to be larger in size and fewer in number than those at lower levels. Occasionally eating seafood lower on the food chain can reduce pressure on higher species and make better use of protein sources. For example, it takes approximately 10,000 kilograms of sardines to produce one kilogram of farm-raised tuna. Consider eating sardines, anchovies or farmed tilapia - fish that live off algae or plants.

6. Keep up to date on fisheries management issues and support initiatives that improve fisheries through responsible management, conservation, fishing practices and fishing gear. Turtle Excluder Devices (TEDs), for example, are a fishing gear modification that allows larger animals like sea turtles and sharks to pass through shrimp trawl nets.

7. Be sure your country has implemented the United Nations (UN) Code of Conduct for Responsible Fisheries and related International Plans of Action (IPOA). These voluntary measures aim to ensure the effective conservation and management of living aquatic resources. A major focus of these actions is to halt illegal, unreported and unregulated (IUU) fishing, which can cause problems for international fisheries management. If your country hasn't implemented the Code and a national action plan, encourage the government to do so. For more information, visit the UN Food and Agriculture Organization (FAO) website at http://www.fao.org/fi/agreem/codecond/codecon.asp.

8. Support the establishment of Marine Protected Areas (MPAs). Research indicates that properly designed MPAs preserve biodiversity while providing refuge and nursery grounds for fish species. These MPAs also have the potential to increase fish stocks, and therefore fishing, outside MPA boundaries.

9. Think twice before starting a marine aquarium hobby. Unless aquarium or ornamental fisheries are carefully and responsibly managed, collection of these species for captive display often damages coral reefs and marine species. Serious concerns include destructive capture methods, overexploitation and high mortality rates during transportation. Another serious issue is the inappropriate release of marine species into non-indigenous environments. This is thought, for example, to account for the introduction of the lionfish to the western Atlantic sea basin.

Project AWARE Foundation supports publication of the Responsible Marine Aquarist book by the Marine Conservation Society. This book addresses concerns, raises awareness of conservation and management issues and summarizes ways that these fisheries are monitored and regulated. For more information visit www.mcsuk.org. Note that freshwater aquariums are far less environmentally damaging because the majority of popular freshwater aquarium fish are bred in captivity.

10. Educate your family, friends and coworkers. Tell them why you support sustainable fisheries and other responsible practices regarding taking from the sea, and how they can help make a difference. Consumers, through their voices and pocketbooks, have the power to make positive changes — but only if they make the effort.

Feeding Aquatic Animals and Fish

To the uninformed, feeding aquatic animals might sound like a positive interaction with wildlife. It surprises many people to learn that in both terrestrial and aquatic ecosystems, feeding animals is generally more detrimental than beneficial to both the animals and the ecosystems. It's for this reason that in many areas, feeding fish or other animals is *strictly prohibited* – as prohibited as underwater hunting. There are several reasons why feeding can be harmful.

1. **The animals will come to associate humans with food.** This can be potentially hazardous to humans if the animals are large predators like sharks. Instead of fleeing or keeping their distance as they would naturally, they approach humans expecting to feed.

2. **The animals may stop feeding on their natural food.** Every creature in an ecosystem plays a role, one of which may be controlling the population of another species. When animals stop eating their natural prey, the prey species may overpopulate and cause a chain reaction of ecological changes, such as over-consuming the species they feed on.

3. **Feeding may cause population shifts.** Many aquatic animals are intelligent and quickly learn that they can get an easy handout by returning to a feeding area. This can cause population shifts in several ways. One way is that species concentrate in the feeding area, reducing local populations in the surrounding area. When the feeding stops, the concentration of predators can cause overfeeding on local prey species. Another issue is that limited availability of food helps control a species' population. Feeding essentially removes this limit, allowing the animals to grow and reproduce far more than they would naturally.

4. **The animals may lose their natural fears and become vulnerable.** When animals lose their natural fear of humans, they can fall prey to underwater hunting because they'll swim right up to hunters. This is a problem with feeding game species where taking game is legal. Even where hunting is prohibited, animals coming out of their normal protective environments to feed become vulnerable to their natural predators in numbers and circumstances that would not normally occur. This also disrupts the local ecosystem.

5. **Animals may get sick from eating foods they're not capable of digesting.** A good example of this is that many fish cannot digest carbohydrates, yet will eat carbohydrate foods provided to them. The human-provided food not only doesn't give the animal any or enough nutrients, but may dissuade it from eating natural prey.

6. **Animals may get sick or die from eating plastic bags or containers.** Unfortunately, many animals treat anything that smells like food as food. When plastic bags or other packaging gets loose in the water, fish and other creatures may swallow them, causing blockages in their digestive system. Severe blockage can directly kill an animal, or weaken it so it becomes vulnerable to predation.

Attracting predators such as sharks or rays by chumming or feeding provides opportunities to see creatures you rarely see otherwise, but carries the aforementioned risks. For these reasons, any form of attracting these animals should only be carried out or directly supervised by professionals experienced in interactions with those animals.

Photograph © Budd Riker

Any form of attracting sharks and rays should only be carried out, or directly supervised by professionals experienced in interactions with those animals.

Environmentally Responsible Diving Techniques

When you first became a PADI Open Water Diver, chances are your instructor emphasized environmentally responsible techniques. Among other things, you probably learned that it's important to swim well above sensitive bottoms, to not touch coral or other fragile organisms, and to weight yourself properly. Let's review these techniques and look at them in more detail.

1. **Dive a tight kit.** Mount clips and lanyards as necessary on your gear – SPG, alternate second stage, accessories, etc. – so you can secure them to your BCD (never to a weight belt) so nothing dangles. Put accessories in pockets when possible.

Dive a tight kit. Mount clips and lanyards to your gear so you can secure them to your BCD.

Diving streamlined benefits the environment because dangling, dragging equipment damages sensitive aquatic life. And, "danglies" have other drawbacks, such as damaging your gear, increasing your profile so you expend more energy and air, and cluttering your rig so it's harder to locate what you need when you need it. A dragging alternate air source can fill with sand or mud, rendering it unusable in an emergency. Lots of protruding gear can make it easier to get snagged and tangled if you're diving around monofilament, kelp, etc.

2. **Stay neutrally buoyant and in the water column, well off the bottom.** Swim in a level, horizontal position with your legs parallel to the bottom or angled slightly upward. This is the best way of avoiding accidentally damaging aquatic life with an errant kick or a misplaced hand.

3. **Avoid diving over weighted.** Your BCD may offset extra weight, but there's more to it than that. Extra weight and the buoyancy to offset it tend to shift your center of gravity down, so your body position tends to be feet-low instead of horizontal. Not only does this waste energy while swimming, but it makes it more likely that you'll damage things with your fin tips. It also means more work controlling your buoyancy because you have a larger air volume that expands and contracts as you change depth.

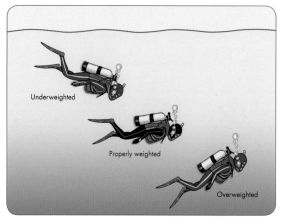

Avoid diving over weighted. Although your BCD can offset excess weight, the added lead and buoyancy tend to shift you into an undesirable feet-low position.

4. **Shift from a feet first descent to a horizontal swimming position well above the bottom.** Many divers prefer to descend feet first. Just remember to get your feet up and switch to a horizontal position before you get too close to the bottom.

5. **Avoid kicking up sand or silt.** This is bad for visibility, inconsiderate of other divers, and it can kill or damage organisms – particularly corals and other sensitive sedentary organisms. Silt settling on them can block sunlight or choke openings used for breathing and feeding. Disturbing the sediment may also put nutrients into the water that would otherwise remain buried.

6. **Be cautious what you touch with your fins, knees and hands.** This is important not only to avoid accidental damage to the environment, but also to avoid being bitten or stung. If you need to touch or kneel on the bottom, look for an insensitive area away from easily damaged organisms. But, remember that even apparently barren sand or mud is home to countless creatures, so look closely and be cautious before you settle even then.

7. **Swim slowly and calmly.** As mentioned earlier, you'll see more if you move as though you're part of the environment. Aquatic animals are generally graceful and swim without abrupt, jerky movements; the more you move like they do, the more you blend in with your surroundings and the more natural behaviors you'll see.

Exercise 5 – Human Interactions with Aquatic Life

1. Passively interacting with aquatic life means (check all that apply):
   - ☐ a. just watching it.
   - ☐ b. minimizing disrupting its natural behaviors.
   - ☐ c. touching or handling it without harming it.
   - ☐ d. diving only in fresh water.

2. You can responsibly touch aquatic life (check all that apply):
   - ☐ a. if you don't cause a significant disruption to the organism's normal behavior.
   - ☐ b. if doing so will not harm you or it.
   - ☐ c. if doing so will provide a meaningful benefit.
   - ☐ d. if the organism is relatively tame.

3. With respect to underwater hunting or any other practice that involves directly or indirectly taking aquatic life, you should (check all that apply):
   - ☐ a. follow all applicable laws conservatively.
   - ☐ b. do without when in doubt about taking something.

   - ☐ c. buy aquarium fish, shells or other animals from appropriately licensed, responsible dealers .
   - ☐ d. buy seafood from responsible sources and not buy species that are at risk.

4. Feeding aquatic animals in the wild (check all that apply):
   - ☐ a. is good for the animals.
   - ☐ b. benefits the environment by creating a nutritional surplus.
   - ☐ c. encourages natural behaviors.
   - ☐ d. may cause ecological imbalances and harm the animals.

5. Diving techniques that help you preserve sensitive bottom dwelling organisms include (check all that apply):
   - ☐ a. diving with a tight kit.
   - ☐ b. diving slightly over weighted to shift your head down.
   - ☐ c. staying neutrally buoyant, well off the bottom.
   - ☐ d. None of the above.

How'd you do?
1. a, b. *2.* a, b, c. *3.* a, b, c, d. *4.* d. *5.* a, c.

The Project AWARE *Foundation*

Divers and Snorkelers: The Natural Ambassadors

It is almost unavoidable for people who regularly put on masks and venture underwater to begin to notice both short and long term changes in the aquatic realm, be it marine or fresh water. Intimate familiarity with the underwater world makes divers natural ambassadors for the aquatic environment. Today, they are some of the strongest supporters of programs and initiatives that include volunteer monitoring, underwater and beach cleanups, marine parks and protected areas, and legislative actions to support sustainable fisheries and protect endangered habitats and species.

To harness each diver's potential as an advocate and protector of the aquatic environment, PADI introduced Project AWARE (Aquatic World Awareness, Responsibility and Education) initiative in 1989.

The Project AWARE Foundation

What began as an environmental ethic formed into the Project AWARE Foundation, a registered nonprofit environmental organization that involves divers and water enthusiasts in projects and activities to conserve underwater environments. The Foundation also supports research, education and conservation projects through its established grant program.

Since the nonprofit designation in 1992, Project AWARE has created an international presence with offices in the United Kingdom, Australia, Switzerland and Japan. You can join the team of environmental divers and contribute to conservation by becoming

> ### Study Objectives
>
> Underline/highlight the answers to these questions as you read:
>
> 1. Why are divers and snorkelers the natural ambassadors for the aquatic environment?
> 2. What is the Project AWARE Foundation?
> 3. What is Project AWARE Foundation's mission and purpose?
> 4. What steps are the Project AWARE Foundation taking to protect the aquatic world in partnership with PADI?

a Project AWARE Patron. Project AWARE Patrons take action for the underwater environment and their donations support conservation and data collection initiatives. All patrons receive a subscription to Project AWARE's email newsletter containing information about conservation activities and action alerts from around the world related to the underwater environment.

Through Project AWARE, each year nearly a million people worldwide are exposed to environmental awareness through interactions with PADI Professionals. For up-to-date information, visit Project AWARE Foundation online at www.projectaware.org.

Project AWARE Foundation's Mission and Purpose

Project AWARE is a nonprofit organization dedicated to conserving underwater environments through education, advocacy and action. Project AWARE partners with divers and water enthusiasts to protect aquatic environments around the world. The Project AWARE Foundation involves divers in environmental projects, activities and campaigns working toward global conservation solutions.

Project AWARE Foundation and PADI

The Project AWARE Foundation is an independent donations based charity that, in partnership with the global PADI family, strives to protect the aquatic world by emphasizing environmentally sound approaches to dive practices, dive operations and dive skills. These environmentally sound practices include mooring buoy use, responsible boating practices, buoyancy control, proper techniques and equipment placement for underwater photography, responsible wreck diving guidelines and dive training programs including this course. Project AWARE implements global initiatives to expand diver participation in conservation activities and data collection including underwater cleanups, coral reef monitoring, shark sightings and identification, and environmental education and advocacy. Project AWARE works towards empowering children to get involved in environmental solutions through the Foundation's AWARE Kids program. Finally, Project AWARE aims at increasing the implementation of sustainable business practices and expanding financial support for the aquatic environment.

Exercise 6 – The Project AWARE Foundation

1. Divers and snorkelers are the natural ambassadors for the aquatic environment as they have (check all that apply):
   - ☐ a. intimate familiarity with the underwater world.
   - ☐ b. masks to see underwater.
   - ☐ c. made changes to the aquatic realm.
   - ☐ d. a lot of potential.

2. The Project AWARE Foundation is a registered nonprofit environmental organization that involves divers and water enthusiasts in projects and activities to conserve underwater environments.
   - ☐ True   ☐ False

3. Project AWARE Foundation's mission is to (check all that apply):
   - ☐ a. charge divers and water enthusiasts an access fee to interact with the aquatic environment.
   - ☐ b. conserve underwater environments through education, advocacy and action.

How'd you do?
1. a. 2. True 3. b.

Special Activities and *Aquatic Life*

One of the cool things about diving is that you can use it to enjoy the beauty of the underwater world in many different ways through special activities. You can put your skills as a PADI Underwater Naturalist to use on any dive and apply it with most specialties. There are three specialties, however, that deserve extra attention from an underwater naturalist's point of view.

Underwater Photography/Videography

Shooting underwater photos or video is a natural interest for anyone interested in the aquatic world's natural splendor. It's a very rewarding activity that goes hand-in-hand with being a PADI Underwater Naturalist because you can document your observations for further study later, and to share with diving and nondiving friends.

Underwater imaging is particularly useful when you want to examine an organism after a dive to help determine a species, or when you want to document a particular behavior. There are times when you can use your images to help scientists. For example, by submitting your photos to the Whale Shark Project (see www.projectaware.org for details) you can help scientists monitor this fish.

Study Objectives

Underline/highlight the answers to these questions as you read:

1. What should you do to minimize your effects on aquatic life while taking underwater photos or video?

2. How do you use a diver propulsion vehicle (DPV) so that you interact responsibly with the underwater environment?

3. How does your experience in night diving improve your ability to interact responsibly with aquatic life, as well as your awareness of it?

4. How does your participation in aquatic life monitoring activities increase your knowledge and contribute to conservation?

A few techniques help minimize the possibility of accidentally damaging aquatic life while shooting, making this an activity that's a relatively passive interaction if you adhere to them.

The first technique is to remember you're a diver before you're a photographer/videographer. This means making sure you continue to use proper diving techniques, even while shooting. Pay particular attention to where your hands and fins are, especially because it's easy to end up in a vertical position while shooting. Be cautious to not stir up the bottom or kick anything living. And, take care of yourself, too, by maintaining buddy contact and frequently checking your instruments and location.

Second, never capture, move, harass or otherwise damage organisms for the sake of creating images. Not only is this irresponsible and unreasonable, but images that show an organism in an unnatural state will often be obvious, making this a poor shooting technique anyway.

Third, be cautious when leading a subject by swimming ahead of it, especially when shooting video. This usually gets you swimming backwards, which makes it easy to run into things and damage them with your cylinder, not to mention hurt yourself. If there's a good reason to use this technique, have a buddy swim ahead to stop you before you collide with something.

If you've never tried underwater photography or video, ask your PADI Dive Center or Resort about the PADI Digital Underwater Photographer or Underwater Videographer courses. Underwater imaging is a fun way to revisit underwater sights and share them.

PADI *Digital Underwater Photographer Manual*

Learn more...

Underwater imaging is a relatively passive interaction, provided you use the proper techniques.

Ten Tips for Underwater Photographers

1. Photograph with Care
Dive carefully, because many aquatic creatures are fragile regardless of size. Improper techniques while taking or editing photos underwater can damage sensitive aquatic life and harm fragile organisms with the bump of a camera or cylinder, swipe of a fin or even the touch of a hand.

2. Dive Neutrally Buoyant
Camera systems may add negative or positive buoyancy. Make sure to secure photo and dive equipment, and to be properly weighted to avoid contact with reefs or other sensitive habitat. Practice buoyancy control and photography skills in a pool before swimming near sensitive and fragile environments.

3. Resist Temptation
Avoid touching, handling, feeding, chasing or riding aquatic life. Avoid altering an organism's location to get the "perfect" shot. Many aquatic creatures are shy and easily stressed. Moving one may interrupt feeding, disturb mating or provoke aggression in a normally nonaggressive species. In the end, it may be obvious what you did anyway, making the photo less than desirable.

4. Easy Does It
While diving, move slowly and deliberately through the water. Be patient and still while photographing – allow organisms to show their natural behavior for a more significant and meaningful shot.

5. Sharpen Your Skills
Make sure the difficulty of the dive and the environmental conditions are appropriate for your current skills and comfort level. Avoid grabbing onto the reef to stabilize yourself for a shot. Enroll in the PADI Underwater Photographer, Digital Underwater Photographer and Peak Performance Buoyancy Specialty courses to become a more skilled and successful photographer.

6. Be Informed
Be aware of local regulations and protocols regarding behavior around marine mammals and other species before entering the water. These regulations protect creatures with the goal of preserving them for future generations.

7. Be an AWARE Diver
Take the AWARE - Coral Reef Conservation or Project AWARE Specialty Diver courses to learn more about sustainable dive techniques and to increase knowledge about the environment you're photographing.

8. Take Only Pictures, Leave Only Bubbles
Avoid souvenir collection. Nearly everything found in the aquatic realm is alive or will be used by a living creature. Removing specimens such as corals and shells can disturb the delicate balance and quickly deplete dive sites of both their resources and their beauty. The wonderful thing about photography is that you can capture this beauty and take it with you without disturbing it.

9. Share Your Images
Use images for conservation by reporting environmental disturbances or destruction using your photographs as evidence. Assist scientific research and improve resource management by contributing your photos to The Whale Shark Project and other monitoring programs. You may also submit your photos to Project AWARE. Your images have the power to change perspectives and influence conservation.

10. Conserve the Adventure
Join Project AWARE Foundation, a nonprofit environmental organization dedicated to conserve underwater environments through education, advocacy and action.

Diver Propulsion Vehicles (DPVs)

Diver propulsion vehicles (DPVs – a.k.a. "scooters") are nothing new to diving. The first DPVs came out in the late 1950s and early 1960s, years before the modern BCD, SPG and dive computers. But, it is only in the last few years that advances in battery technology and electronics have started to provide the performance, size and price options necessary for them to become widely popular.

DPVs are great tools for divers, as well as a lot of fun. They allow you to explore a wider area, and all things being equal, give you longer bottom times by reducing your energy expenditure, thus saving air. As a PADI Underwater Naturalist, you can use DPVs to survey wide areas of reef, or to find specific organisms or habitats that interest you.

Like many tools, however, the rise of DPVs brings with it some concerns. DPVs move you quickly, creating more potential for impact damage if you collide with the reef. Their propellers can stir up the bottom far more and over a greater area than kicking alone. Fortunately, if you're aware of these issues, you can ride your DPV avoiding them.

Just as you swim well above the bottom, DPV well above the bottom. This greatly reduces the chance you'll run into something. It also puts you where you're less likely to frighten shy aquatic animals. If you want to look closely at something, stop and descend without power.

Dive properly weighted with your buoyancy adjusted so you pilot the DPV level. If you're negatively buoyant, you tend to point the DPV upward to hold you off the bottom. This not only wastes power, but aims the prop wash at the bottom, potentially stirring up silt.

When you stop and park your DPV, be careful to put it where it won't rest or bump into anything sensitive. Allow ample space around aquatic vegetation like kelp that your DPV can accidentally draw into the propeller.

Finally, remember that DPVs make noise, which some divers as well as wildlife find objectionable. Drive DPVs so that you don't frighten wildlife, and in a manner that's courteous to other divers. To learn more about DPV use and scootering, see your PADI Instructor about the PADI Diver Propulsion Vehicle course.

 PADI *Diver Propulsion Vehicle Manual*

Learn more...

Night Diving

If you're interested in underwater wildlife, it almost goes without saying that you're interested in night diving – even if you've never tried it and it sounds eerie to you. Night diving fits well with being a PADI Underwater Naturalist because it improves your ability to interact responsibly with aquatic life, as well as increases your awareness.

When you're diving after dark, you don't usually go as far. This, and the fact that you only see where you shine your light, focuses your attention on a smaller area, and helps you see more detail. Because it's easier to bump into things in the dark, night diving teaches you to be more aware of body position and where you're putting your hands and feet. You become more cautious about

DPVs are fun and great tools for exploring the underwater world, but pilot them responsibly so you don't damage or frighten aquatic organisms.

touching things by accident, which is a good habit to have during the day as well.

From an underwater naturalist perspective, night diving reveals a different side of the same ecosystems and sites you see during the day. Familiar animals display different behaviors at night, and nocturnal organisms become active and emerge from hiding. If you're patient and watch closely, you'll witness processes and behaviors you would never see during the day. As with other specialty activities, the best way to get started with night diving is by taking the PADI Night Diver course, or with the Night Adventure Dive in the PADI Adventures in Diving program.

Night diving fits well with being a PADI Underwater Naturalist because it can improve your dive skills and allow you to see animals and behaviors you would never see during the day.

Monitoring and Conservation Activities

Participating in monitoring and assessing aquatic life increases your knowledge and understanding of the underwater environment because every time you dive you are bound to encounter new organisms and behaviors.

Your observations can inform science and management decisions by providing vital information on the local, regional and international status of threatened or endangered species. For example, participating in Project AWARE's CoralWatch monitoring provides vital information on the bleaching trends of coral reefs world wide. Divers interested in learning more about coral reefs can take the AWARE Coral Reef Conservation course.

Exercise 7 – Special Activities and Aquatic Life

1. To minimize effects on aquatic life while shooting underwater photos or video (check all that apply):
   - [ ] a. be a diver first.
   - [ ] b. be careful where you put your hands and feet.
   - [ ] c. never capture, harass or move an organism for the sake of shot .
   - [ ] d. be careful when leading a subject by swimming ahead of it.

2. When riding a DPV, to minimize effects on aquatic life (check all that apply):
   - [ ] a. stay well above the bottom.
   - [ ] b. be careful where you park it.
   - [ ] c. avoid letting prop wash stir up the bottom.
   - [ ] d. be careful not to scare fish and animals.

3. Night diving (check all that apply):
   - [ ] a. can improve your ability to interact responsibly with aquatic life.
   - [ ] b. may increase your awareness of aquatic life.
   - [ ] c. teaches you to be more aware of your body position.
   - [ ] d. lets you observe creatures and behaviors you don't see during the day.

How'd you do?
1. a, b, c, d. 2. a, b, c, d. 3. a, b, c, d.

Participating in a Project AWARE CoralWatch dive activity is easy and informative, and allows you to contribute valuable information to a global database.

Underwater Naturalist Specialty Course
Open Water Dives

The following outlines the two dives you'll make as part of your PADI Underwater Naturalist Specialty course. Your instructor may rearrange skill sequences in each dive, or may add more dives as necessary to meet your needs, desires, course requirements and the environmental conditions.

Dive 1

- Knowledge Review/Briefing
- Predive Procedures – Above Water Skill Practice
- Dive 1 Tasks
  - Passively observe aquatic life.
  - Apply diving techniques used to preserve bottom dwelling organisms and minimize disturbance of all aquatic life.
  - Locate and identify, by common or scientific name, at least two local aquatic plants (one for freshwater).
  - Locate, observe and identify, by common or scientific name, at least four local aquatic invertebrate animals (one for freshwater).
  - Locate, observe and identify, by common or scientific name, at least five local aquatic vertebrate animals (two for freshwater).
- Post-dive Procedures
- Debrief
- Log Dive

Dive 2

- Knowledge Review/Briefing

- Predive Procedures – Above Water Skill Practice

- Dive 2 Tasks

  - Passively observe aquatic life.

  - Apply diving techniques used to preserve bottom-dwelling organisms and minimize disturbance of all aquatic life.

  - Identify and observe as many examples of symbiotic and predator/prey relationships as possible.
    [Review the symbiotic relationships: mutualism, commensalism and parasitism.]

  - Locate as many indications of impact by man on the local aquatic environment as possible, and evaluate the possible cause.

- Post-dive Procedures

- Debrief

- Log Dive

Name _____   Date _____

Knowledge Review — Part I

Note to student: The first half of this Knowledge Review is the same Knowledge Review in the Underwater Naturalist section of *Adventures in Diving*. If your instructor has the first half on file from your PADI Adventure Diver or PADI Advanced Open Water Diver course, your instructor may have you complete only the second half of this Knowledge Review.

Answer the following questions and bring this completed Knowledge Review with you to your next training session.

1. Define the terms *ecology* and *ecosystem*.

    Ecology:

    Ecosystem:

2. List three physical/structural differences between aquatic ecosystems and terrestrial ecosystems.

    1. _____

    2. _____

    3. _____

3. Identify the most common cause of aquatic animal "attacks."

4. Describe an accurate view of potentially dangerous aquatic animals.

5. List four inaccurate ways people may perceive aquatic animals.

    1. _____

    2. _____

    3. _____

    4. _____

6. Explain how to interact passively with aquatic organisms.

7. Explain how and when you can responsibly touch or handle aquatic animals.

8. Explain why divers should not ride aquatic animals.

9. Why should divers avoid feeding aquatic animals?

10. Describe the diving techniques that you should use to preserve bottom dwelling organisms and to minimize disturbing all aquatic life.

Student Diver Statement:
Any questions I answered incorrectly or incompletely, I've had explained to me, and I understand what I missed.

Name _____   Date _____

Name _____ Date _____

Knowledge Review — Part II

Answer the following questions and bring this completed Knowledge Review with you to your next training session.

11. Why do scientists classify organisms and what two taxa does an organism's scientific name represent?

12. What do taxonomists base their classification on and what are the seven taxa into which organisms are classified?

13. What is the most common problem when classifying organisms into different categories?

14. What are the six-kingdom and three-domain systems of classification?

15. What is *symbiosis?*

16. Define the terms *mutualism, commensalism* and *parasitism* and give an example of each in the aquatic environment.

Mutualism: _____

_____

Commensalism: _____

_____

Parasitism: _____

_____

17. What is Project AWARE Foundation's mission and purpose? Give an example of what Project AWARE is doing to protect the aquatic world in partnership with PADI.

18. What should you do to minimize your effects on aquatic life while taking underwater photos or video?

19. How do you use a DPV so that you interact responsibly with the underwater environment?

20. How does experience in night diving improve your ability to interact responsibility with aquatic life, as well as your awareness of it?

Student Diver Statement:

Any questions I answered incorrectly or incompletely, I've had explained to me, and I understand what I missed.

Name _____ Date _____

PADI courses have the unique distinction of meeting academic excellence criteria as established by university and vocational accreditation bodies. Find out how you can get credit for your PADI education!

Australia

PADI Divers may receive credit toward various certificates and diplomas for several PADI courses within the Australian national training system. The following training providers recognise certain PADI and Emergency First Response (EFR) courses — Technical and Further Education, South Australia; Australia Fisheries Academy, South Australia; Victorian Tertiary Admissions Center, Victoria; and the Western Australia Curriculum Council. For more information, go to: www.padi.com/padi/en/footerlinks/collegecredits.aspx

Canada

The British Columbia Ministry of Education (External Credentials Program for Industrial and Occupational Courses) has approved the PADI Open Water Diver (2 credits), PADI Advanced or Adventures in Diving Program (4 credits) and PADI Rescue Diver (4 credits) courses for school credit. Grade 10, 11 and 12 students who have been certified in these PADI courses simply present their PADI certification card to the school administration to apply for credit. For information on receiving credit contact your school's administration. On an individual, merit-base case, divers in Canada may also receive credit for PADI courses through the USA-based American Council on Education's College Credit Recommendation Service as noted under "United States."

England, Wales and Northern Ireland

PADI Open Water Scuba Instructors can apply to PADI for the Certificate in Scuba Instruction, a Vocationally Related Qualification (VRQ) accredited at Level 3 on the National Qualifications Framework in England, Wales and Northern Ireland, by the Qualifications and Curriculum Authority (QCA) for England, Department for Education, Lifelong Learning and Skills (DELLS) for Wales and the Council for the Curriculum, Examinations and Assessment (CCEA) for Northern Ireland. The certificate may be accepted by Further Education institutions as proof of eligibility for attendance at higher level courses. Contact ie@padi.co.uk for an application form.

Europe

Divers have received credit for PADI courses in mainland Europe academic institutions and through the military; but since there is no formal recognition process, these have been individual cases. For more information or for a specific request, contact PADI Europe at training@padi.ch

Japan

Those who want to teach diving in Japanese school systems (colleges, universities, vocational schools, etc.) undergo general and specialized course work and testing to become authorized by the Japan Sports Association (JASA), under the jurisdiction of the Ministry of Education, Culture, Sports, Science and Technology. PADI Open Water Scuba Instructors are exempt from this specialized course and test, and can attain JASA authorization by taking a general course and certification test. For more information go to www.japan-sports.or.jp/english

New Zealand

PADI Divers may qualify to receive recognition through a New Zealand Qualification Authority accredited provider. Open Water Divers, Advanced Open Water Diver, Rescue Diver qualify for the National Certificate of Diving: Foundational Skills; Divemaster and Open Water Scuba Instructors qualify for the National Certificate of Diving: Leadership; and Specialty Instructors qualify for the National Certificate of Diving: Instruction. For more information, go to www.padi.com/padi/en/footerlinks/collegecredits.aspx

United States

The American Council on Education's College Credit Recommendation Service (ACE CREDIT) has evaluated and recommended college credit for 15 PADI courses, 3 DSAT courses, and 1 Emergency First Response course. The American Council on Education, the major coordinating body for all the nation's higher education institutions, seeks to provide leadership and a unifying voice on key higher education issues and to influence public policy through advocacy, research, and program initiatives. For more information on ACE CREDIT recommendations, and to order an official PADI transcript, go to www.padi.com/padi/en/footerlinks/collegecredits.aspx or contact PADI Americas at training@padi.com